Shakespeare
The Animated Tales

Abridged by Leon Garfield

'O Romeo, Romeo, wherefore art thou Romeo?'

'To be or not to be, that is the question.'

Other **Egmont Classics** titles

Little House in the Big Woods	Laura Ingalls Wilder
Little House on the Prairie	Laura Ingalls Wilder
On the Banks of Plum Creek	Laura Ingalls Wilder
The Wool-Pack	Cynthia Harnett
The Load of Unicorn	Cynthia Harnett
The Animals of Farthing Wood	Colin Dann
The Box of Delights	John Masefield
The Midnight Folk	John Masefield
National Velvet	Enid Bagnold
The Yearling	Marjorie Kinnan Rawlings
The Wind in the Willows	Kenneth Grahame
The Apprentices	Leon Garfield
Complete Poems for Children	James Reeves

Shakespeare
The Animated Tales

Abridged by Leon Garfield

EGMONT

This collection first published in Great Britain 2002
by Egmont Books Limited
239 Kensington High Street, London W8 6SA

Combined volume © Shakespeare Animated Films, Christmas Films
and Soyuzmultfilm 2002
Cover illustration copyright © Jane Human 2002
Inside illustration copyright © Rosamund Fowler 2002

The moral rights of the illustrators have been asserted

ISBN 0 7497 4813 3

10 9 8 7 6 5 4 3 2 1

A CIP catalogue record for this title is available from the British Library

Typeset in Great Britain by Dorchester Typesetting Group Ltd

Printed and bound in Great Britain
by Cox & Wyman Ltd, Reading, Berkshire

Contents

Foreword by Samuel West   1

What They Said of Him   2

The Plays

   A Midsummer Night's Dream   3

   Julius Caesar   43

   Twelfth Night   71

   Othello   113

   The Taming of the Shrew   146

   Romeo and Juliet   175

   As You Like It   216

   Hamlet   245

   The Winter's Tale   288

   Richard III   319

   The Tempest   350

   Macbeth   391

William Shakespeare   435

The Theatre in Shakespeare's Day   439

Foreword

I started acting at school, and there I discovered a love for it that I hope many of those reading *Shakespeare – The Animated Tales* for the first time will share.

We're often told we must live in the real world. But this isn't the real world. This is Illyria, lady (or Elsinore, man). Why should we pretend? Why should we act at all? Because to act, to get into someone else's shoes, and use their words, you have to look at things from their point of view. And when you practise this sympathy, it changes your life. If you've played a 14-year-old Romeo bawling over his banishment on Friar Lawrence's floor, exiled from the only thing he loves, you never feel the same way about asylum seekers. If you've played Shylock, you can never be anti-Semitic. The world turns and Shakespeare's characters turn with it, in timeless, complex, sometimes difficult ways that we nevertheless recognise as truth.

As adults we sometimes lose the ability to pretend, and theatre can re-introduce us. Whether we do it professionally or not, we should 'play' more often. It makes us better people.

If you perform these plays, it'll be an unforgettable experience. And those of us watching must exercise our imaginations, and go beyond the everyday into a world that is, and is not, our own.

Samuel West

What They Said of Him

One will ever find, in searching his works, new cause for astonishment and admiration.

GOETHE

Shakespeare was a writer of all others the most calculated to make his readers better as well as wiser.

SAMUEL TAYLOR COLERIDGE

An overstrained enthusiasm is more pardonable with respect to Shakespeare than the want of it; for our admiration cannot easily surpass his genius.

WILLIAM HAZLITT

It required three hundred years for England to begin to hear those two words that the whole world cries in her ear – William Shakespeare.

VICTOR HUGO

He has left nothing to be said about nothing or anything.

JOHN KEATS

The stream of time, which is continually washing the dissoluble fabrics of other poets, passes without injury by the adamant of Shakespeare.

SAMUEL JOHNSON

A Midsummer Night's Dream

Of all Shakespeare's plays, this must be the best-loved. It is the story of a night of confusions in a haunted wood. Four young lovers, trying to resolve their passions, and six worthy workmen, trying to rehearse a play, stumble about in its magical moonlight, while the powerful spirits of the wood, who have mysterious affairs of their own, play havoc with their hearts and minds.

It is the story of a magical flower whose juice plays strange tricks on the eyes, turning love to hate, and hate to love. It is the story of fools and fairies, and, above all, of Bottom, the weaver, whose head has been magically transformed into the head of an ass, and who, for the space of a glorious hour, finds himself in the arms of Titania, Queen of the Fairies, while Oberon, her dread lord, steals away her beloved Indian page.

Shakespeare wrote it at about the same time as *Romeo and Juliet*, when he was thirty-one or two; and indeed the two plays have much in common, one, at times, seeming almost the comic counterpart of the other.

It is a play about illusion and the transfiguring power of imagination. At the very beginning we are told that there is

3

nothing to choose between two young men. 'I am, my lord, as well derived as he, as well possessed,' says one to the duke who is judging the case, 'my fortunes every way as fairly ranked.' But nonetheless, Hermia's father has chosen one, and Hermia herself has chosen the other. 'I would my father looked but with my eyes,' says Hermia; while the duke advises, 'Rather your eyes must with his judgement look', leaving poor Hermia to wail hopelessly, 'O hell, to choose love by another's eyes!'

And then, in the midnight wood, eyes are bewitched; love turns to hatred, and scorn to breathless, panting love. Illusion reigns supreme; not even the Fairy Queen is spared, for she, her sight enchanted, sees in donkey-headed Bottom a being of matchless beauty.

And Bottom, who cannot see that he has an ass's head, suffers from the illusion – as do we all – that others see him as he supposes himself. Yet to Bottom, Bully Bottom, the best man in all Athens, must go the last word in summing up our feelings about this play. 'I have had a most rare vision,' he says; and so indeed have we.

The Characters in the Play

in order of appearance

EGEUS	*Hermia's father*
THESEUS	*Duke of Athens*
HERMIA	*in love with Lysander*
DEMETRIUS	*young courtiers, in love with Hermia*
LYSANDER	
HELENA	*in love with Demetrius*
PETER QUINCE	*a carpenter, Prologue in the Interlude*
NICK BOTTOM	*a weaver, Pyramus in the Interlude*
FRANCIS FLUTE	*a bellows-mender, Thisbe in the Interlude*
SNUG	*a joiner, Lion in the Interlude*
OBERON	*King of the Fairies*
TITANIA	*Queen of the Fairies*
PUCK	*Oberon's jester and lieutenant*
ATTENDANTS	*to Titania*
TOM SNOUT	*a tinker, Wall in the Interlude*
HIPPOLYTA	*Queen of the Amazons, betrothed to Theseus*
ROBIN STARVELING	*a tailor, Moonshine in the Interlude*
PHILOSTRATE	*Theseus' Master of the Revels*

The curtain rises on Athens, a white and golden city, bright and joyous as a wedding cake. Everywhere there is preparation for the marriage of Duke Theseus to Hippolyta, the queen he has won in battle. But in the midst of all this happiness, there is a speck of misery, like a sour plum . . .

Into the council chamber of the palace, an angry father, Egeus, drags his disobedient daughter, Hermia, to seek justice before the duke and his royal bride.

She will not marry the man of his choice but obstinately prefers another.

After them come the two young men in question: Lysander, the daughter's desire and Demetrius, her father's. Wilfully, she breaks free of Egeus's grasp.

EGEUS

Happy be Theseus, our renowned Duke! Full of vexation come I, with complaint against my child, my daughter Hermia. Stand forth, Demetrius! (*Demetrius, full of virtue, stands forth.*) My noble lord, this man hath my consent to marry her. Stand forth, Lysander! (*Lysander, full of defiance, stands forth.*) And, my gracious Duke, this man hath bewitched the bosom of my child. (*Lysander and Hermia exchange ardent looks.*) Be it so she will not here, before your grace, consent to marry with Demetrius, I beg the ancient privilege of Athens; as she is mine, I may dispose of her, either to this gentleman or to her death.

THESEUS   Be advised, fair maid. Demetrius is a
            worthy gentleman.

HERMIA   So is Lysander. I do entreat your grace to
            pardon me. But I beseech your grace that I may
            know the worst that may befall me in this case,
            if I refuse to wed Demetrius.

THESEUS   Either to die the death, or to abjure for ever the
            society of men. Take time to pause –

            Hermia and Lysander gaze at each other.

DEMETRIUS   Relent, sweet Hermia; and Lysander, yield –

LYSANDER   You have her father's love, Demetrius, let me
            have Hermia's – do you marry him. (*To the
            duke*) I am, my lord, as well-derived as he, and,
            which is more, I am beloved of beauteous
            Hermia. Demetrius, I'll avouch it to his head,
            made love to Nedar's daughter, Helena, and
            won her soul.

THESEUS   I must confess that I have heard so much. But
            Demetrius, come, and come, Egeus. You shall go
            with me. For you, fair Hermia, look you arm
            yourself to fit your fancies to your father's will.

            *They all depart, leaving Hermia and
            Lysander alone.*

7

LYSANDER	Ay me! The course of true love never did run smooth.
HERMIA	If then true lovers have been ever crossed, it stands as an edict in destiny.
LYSANDER	So quick bright things come to confusion. If thou lov'st me, then steal forth thy father's house tomorrow night, and in the wood, a league without the town, there will I stay for thee.
HERMIA	I swear to thee by Cupid's strongest bow, tomorrow truly will I meet with thee.
LYSANDER	Keep promise, love. Look, here comes Helena!

Helena enters, much distracted, for she loves Demetrius even as Hermia loves Lysander but alas with no return.

HERMIA	God speed, fair Helena! Whither away?
HELENA	Call you me fair? That 'fair' again unsay. O teach me how you look, and with what art you sway the motion of Demetrius' heart.
HERMIA	Take comfort: he no more shall see my face.
LYSANDER	Tomorrow night through Athens' gates have we devised to steal.

HERMIA   And in the wood where often you and I were
          wont to lie, there my Lysander and myself
          shall meet. Farewell, sweet playfellow; pray
          thou for us!

          *They all part. Helena lingers and gazes bitterly
          after Hermia.*

HELENA   Ere Demetrius looked on Hermia's eyne, he
          hailed down oaths that he was only mine. I will
          go tell him of fair Hermia's flight! (*Vindictively*)
          Then to the wood . . .

          *So while the preparations for the wedding of Duke
          Theseus occupy his subjects, the four lovers flee the
          city. Meanwhile, in a humble, smoky, candlelit
          room, six worthy workmen of Athens are gathered
          together. They are to prepare a play for the festivities
          of the wedding. If they succeed, they will all be given
          pensions for life; so it is a serious business. The play
          has been chosen: it is Pyramus and Thisbe, a tale of
          tragic lovers.*

          *The company is to be directed by Peter Quince, the
          carpenter. Foremost among his actors is Nick
          Bottom, the weaver. The lesser lights are Flute, the
          bellows-mender, Snout, the tinker, Snug, the joiner,
          and Starveling, the tailor.*

QUINCE   Is all our company here? (*They nod.*) Here is

9

the scroll of every man's name which is thought fit through all Athens to play in our interlude before the Duke and Duchess on his wedding day at night. Answer me as I call you. Nick Bottom, the weaver?

BOTTOM   Ready. Name what part I am for, and proceed.

QUINCE   You, Nick Bottom, are set down for Pyramus.

BOTTOM   What is Pyramus? A lover or a tyrant?

QUINCE   A lover that kills himself, most gallant, for love. Francis Flute, the bellows-mender?

FLUTE   Here, Peter Quince.

QUINCE   Flute, you must take Thisbe on you.

FLUTE   Nay, faith, let me not play a woman: I have a beard coming.

QUINCE   That's all one: you shall play it in a mask –

BOTTOM   Let me play Thisbe too –

QUINCE   No, no; you must play Pyramus; and Flute, you Thisbe. Robin Starveling, the tailor? You must play Thisbe's mother. Tom Snout, the tinker? You, Pyramus' father; myself, Thisbe's father;

Snug, the joiner, you the lion's part.

SNUG   Have you the lion's part written? Pray you, if it
          be, give it to me, for I am slow of study.

QUINCE   You may do it extempore; for it is nothing
          but roaring.

BOTTOM   Let me play the lion too. I will roar that I will
          make the Duke say, 'Let him roar again!'

QUINCE   You can play no part but Pyramus; for Pyramus
          is a sweet-faced man.

BOTTOM   Well, I will undertake it.

QUINCE   Here are your parts, (*he distributes scrolls*) and I
          am to entreat you to con them by tomorrow
          night, and meet me in the palace wood by
          moonlight; there will we rehearse . . .

          *The wood. The moon shines down and tips all the
          leaves with silver. It is a place of mystery. Unseen
          creatures rustle among the bushes, like disturbed
          dreams. Suddenly, in a clearing, a weird
          configuration of tree and leaf becomes a strange,
          threatening figure in a dark cloak. It is Oberon,
          king of the night-time world. At his feet crouches
          Puck, his wicked, grinning henchman, and all
          about are his sharp-eyed goblin servants.*

11

OBERON   Ill met by moonlight, proud Titania.

*Across the glade appears the delicate, glittering
Fairy Queen, accompanied by her glimmering train
of sprites. Among them is a pretty little Indian boy,
guarded like a jewel. The Fairy King and Queen
stare at one another with hostility.*

TITANIA   What, jealous Oberon? Fairies, skip hence! I
have forsworn his bed and company. (*She raises
her hand. Her followers quiver and tremble, about
to depart.*)

OBERON   Tarry, rash wanton! Why should Titania cross
her Oberon? I do but beg a little changeling
boy to be my henchman. (*He points to the
Indian child.*)

TITANIA   Set your heart at rest. The fairy land buys not
the child of me. His mother was a votaress of
my order . . .

OBERON   Give me that boy!

TITANIA   Not for thy fairy kingdom! Fairies, away!

*With a screaming and rushing sound Titania and
her train vanish from the glade.*

OBERON   Well, go thy way; thou shalt not from this grove till I torment thee for this injury. My gentle Puck, come hither . . . (*Puck approaches, Oberon whispers in his crooked ear.*) Fetch me that flower, the herb I showed thee once; the juice of it on sleeping eyelids laid will make or man or woman madly dote upon the next live creature that it sees. Fetch me this herb!

PUCK   I'll put a girdle round about the earth in forty minutes!

Like a whirling leaf, Puck flies off. Oberon smiles.

OBERON   Having once this juice I'll watch Titania when she is asleep, and drop the liquor of it in her eyes; the next thing then she, waking, looks upon – be it on lion, bear or wolf, or bull, on meddling monkey, or on busy ape – she shall pursue it with the soul of love –

He is disturbed by a sudden crashing of branches. Instantly, he becomes invisible. The crashing grows louder and first Demetrius, then Helena, burst into the glade.

DEMETRIUS   I love thee not, therefore pursue me not! Where is Lysander and fair Hermia? Hence, get thee gone, and follow me no more.

HELENA   (*clutching tearfully at him*) I am your spaniel;

13

and Demetrius, the more you beat me, I will
fawn on you. Use me but as your spaniel, spurn
me, strike me, neglect me, lose me; only give
me leave, unworthy as I am, to follow you!

DEMETRIUS   (*flinging her off*) I am sick when I do look
on thee!

HELENA   (*clutching him again*) And I am sick when I look
not on you!

DEMETRIUS   Let me go, or, if thou follow me, do not believe
but I shall do thee mischief in the wood!

*He escapes and plunges away into the wood.
Helena follows, weeping. Oberon becomes
visible again.*

OBERON   Fare thee well, nymph. Ere he do leave this
grove, thou shalt fly him, and he shall seek
thy love.

*Puck returns, as swiftly as he departed. He kneels at
his master's feet, and holds up a purple flower.
Oberon takes it and gazes at it, musingly.*

OBERON   I know a bank where the wild thyme blows,
where oxlips and the nodding violet grows,
quite over-canopied with luscious woodbine,
with sweet musk-roses and with eglantine.

14

There sleeps Titania some time of the night . . .
(*He peers into the depths of the flower.*) With the
juice of this I'll streak her eyes, and make her
full of hateful fantasies. (*Puck laughs delightedly.
Oberon frowns. He takes a petal from the flower
and gives it to Puck.*) Take thou some of it, and
seek through this grove: a sweet Athenian lady
is in love with a disdainful youth; anoint his
eyes; but do it when the next thing he espies
may be the lady. Thou shalt know the man by
the Athenian garments he hath on.

PUCK   Fear not, my lord, your servant shall do so.

*Another part of the moonlit wood: the 'bank where
the wild thyme blows'. Titania reclines upon a
mossy couch. Her attendants watch over her, and
her Indian boy plays happily . . .*

TITANIA   Come now, a roundel and a fairy song . . .

ATTENDANTS   You spotted snakes with double tongue,
        Thorny hedgehogs be not seen;
    Newts and blindworms do no wrong,
        Come not near our fairy queen . . .

*As they sing, Titania closes her eyes and sleeps. The
attendants creep away, taking with them the Indian
boy. Titania is alone. Suddenly Oberon appears. He
smiles, and, bending over his sleeping queen,*

15

*squeezes the magic liquor from the flower upon
her eyelids.*

OBERON   What thou seest when thou dost wake, do it
for thy true love take. Wake when some vile
thing is near.

*Slowly, Oberon vanishes. Titania sleeps on, 'quite
over-canopied with luscious woodbine'. Slowly, she
fades into invisibility. Into the glade, arm in loving
arm, come Hermia and Lysander. They are plainly
weary from walking.*

LYSANDER   We'll rest us, Hermia, if you think it good.

HERMIA   Be it so, Lysander; find you out a bed, for I
upon this couch will rest my head.

*She seats herself. Lysander promptly sits beside her,
very close.*

LYSANDER   One turf shall serve as pillow for us both.

HERMIA   Nay, good Lysander; for my sake, my dear, lie
further off yet.

*He retires, but not by much. Hermia gestures
urgently.*

HERMIA   Lie further off, in human modesty; such

16

separation as may well be said becomes a virtuous bachelor and a maid. (*Lysander at last betakes himself to a satisfactory distance.*) So far be distant; and good night, sweet friend.

They both settle down and, in moments, are asleep. No sooner are their eyes closed than Puck appears.

PUCK   There is he my master said despised the Athenian maid; and here the maiden, sleeping sound, on the dank and dirty ground. Pretty soul, she durst not lie near this lack-love, this kill-courtesy! (*He bends over Lysander and anoints his eyes with juice from the magic flower.*) Churl, upon thine eyes I throw all the power this charm doth owe.

Sounds of a violent approach cause Puck to vanish abruptly. Into the glade rushes Demetrius, followed by the weeping, brush-torn Helena.

DEMETRIUS   I charge thee, hence, and do not haunt me thus!

He plunges on, Helena pauses, and stares fearfully about her

HELENA   O wilt thou darkling leave me? (*Suddenly she spies Lysander.*) But who is here? Lysander on the ground? Dead, or asleep? I see no blood, no wound. Lysander, if you live, good sir, awake!

She bends low over him, and gently shakes him. He opens his magically anointed eyes. Instantly he falls in love with Helena. He looks towards the sleeping Hermia. He frowns and shakes his head. He looks again at Helena, now radiant in his eyes.

LYSANDER Not Hermia, but Helena I love: who will not change a raven for a dove!

He rises and tries to embrace her. Helena leaps back with a squeal of alarm.

HELENA Good troth, you do me wrong, good sooth, you do! Fare you well!

She flies from the glade in great distress. Lysander stares at the sleeping Hermia. His expression is far from loving.

LYSANDER Hermia, sleep thou there, and never mayest thou come Lysander near! (*He gazes after the departed Helena.*) All my powers, address your love and might, to honour Helena and to be her knight!

He pursues Helena. Hermia is left alone. She stirs and frowns, in the grip of a bad dream. She cries out in her sleep –

HERMIA   Help me, Lysander, help me! Pluck this
                crawling serpent from my breast! (*She wakes.*)
                Ay me, for pity! What a dream was there! (*She
                looks about her.*) Lysander! Lysander, lord!
                Alack, where are you! (*She rises and rushes from
                the glade.*)

                *For a moment, the place is quiet; then comes the
                tramp of sturdy feet and, one by one, the Athenian
                workmen, bearing their scrolls, enter the glade.*

QUINCE   Here's a marvellous convenient place for
                our rehearsal.

BOTTOM   (*consulting his scroll*) Peter Quince, there are
                things in this comedy of Pyramus and Thisbe
                that will never please. First, Pyramus must
                draw a sword to kill himself, which the ladies
                cannot abide.

STARVELING   I believe we must leave the killing out, when all
                is done.

BOTTOM   Not a whit; I have a device to make all well.
                Write 'em a prologue, and let the prologue
                seem to say we will do no harm with our
                swords, and that Pyramus is not killed indeed;
                and for the more better assurance, tell him that
                I, Pyramus, am not Pyramus, but Bottom the
                weaver: this will put them out of fear.

19

QUINCE   Well, it shall be so. But there is two hard things: that is, to bring moonlight into a chamber; for, you know, Pyramus and Thisbe meet by moonlight.

BOTTOM   Why, then, you must leave a casement of the great chamber window, where we play, open –

QUINCE   Ay, or else one must come in with a bush of thorn and a lantern, and say he comes to disfigure, or to present the person of Moonshine. (*All nod wisely.*) Then there is another thing: we must have a wall in the great chamber; for Pyramus and Thisbe (says the story) did talk through the chink of a wall.

SNOUT   You can never bring in a wall. What say you, Bottom?

BOTTOM   Some man or other must present Wall; and let him have some plaster, or some loam, or some rough-cast about him to signify Wall.

QUINCE   If that may be, then all is well. Come, sit down every mother's son, and rehearse your parts. Pyramus, you begin . . .

           They disperse themselves about the glade. Puck appears, in grinning invisibility.

PUCK   What hempen homespuns have we swaggering
         here, so near the cradle of the Fairy Queen?
         (*He stays to observe.*)

QUINCE   Speak, Pyramus! Thisbe, stand forth!

         Bottom and Flute confront one another.

BOTTOM   Thisbe, the flowers of odious savours sweet –

QUINCE   Odorous – odorous!

BOTTOM   . . . odorous savours sweet. So hath thy breath,
         my dearest Thisbe dear. (*Quince thumps on the
         ground, as a cue.*) But hark, a voice. Stay thou
         but here awhile, and by and by I will to thee
         appear. (*Exit Bottom into a bush, above which
         hovers Puck.*)

FLUTE   Must I speak now?

QUINCE   Ay, marry, must you!

FLUTE   (*girlishly*) Most radiant Pyramus, most lily-
         white of hue! I'll meet thee, Pyramus, at
         Ninny's tomb.

QUINCE   At Ninus's tomb, man! Why, you must not
         speak yet; that you must answer to Pyramus.
         You speak all your part at once, cues and all!

(He turns to the bush) Pyramus, enter! Your cue is past –

As he speaks, Puck, still hovering above the bush, makes a magic pass with his hands. A pair of large, hairy ears appears poking through the leaves.

QUINCE   Pyramus, enter!

A loud thumping, and Bottom emerges from the bush. But a strangely altered Bottom. In place of his human head is now the head of an ass!

BOTTOM   If I were fair, Thisbe –

Bottom's companions stare at him in stark terror.

QUINCE   O monstrous! O strange! We are haunted! Pray, masters! Fly, masters! Help!

They fly madly from the glade, leaving the weirdly altered Bottom alone.

BOTTOM   Why do they run away?

Briefly, Quince returns, as if to make sure of what he has seen.

QUINCE   Bless thee, Bottom, bless thee! Thou art translated! *(He departs.)*

BOTTOM   I see their knavery: this is to make an ass of me, to fright me if they could . . . (*He begins to walk up and down, to keep his spirits up.*) I will sing, that they shall hear I am not afraid:

> The ousel cock, so black of hue,
> With orange-tawny bill,
> The throstle with his note so true,
> The wren with little quill . . .

As he sings, Titania, sleeping on her mossy couch, becomes visible. Skilfully, Puck leads the singing Bottom towards the Fairy Queen. Titania awakes, and feasts her magically anointed eyes upon the donkey-headed Bottom.

TITANIA   What angel wakes me from my flowery bed? I pray thee, gentle mortal, sing again: mine ear is much enamoured of thy note. So is mine eye enthralled to thy shape, and thy fair virtue's force perforce doth move me on first view to say, to swear, I love thee.

Bottom gazes at the Fairy Queen without surprise; indeed, it would take much to surprise Bottom.

BOTTOM   Methinks, mistress, you should have little reason for that. And yet, to say the truth, reason and love keep little company nowadays. The more the pity that some honest neighbours will not make them friends.

Titania's attendants look on in amazement at this mad infatuation of their mistress. Titania rises from the ground and takes Bottom by the arm.

TITANIA   Thou art as wise as thou art beautiful.

BOTTOM   Not so neither; but if I had wit enough to get out of this wood, I had enough to serve mine own turn.

TITANIA   Out of this wood do not desire to go. Thou shalt remain here, whether thou wilt or no. I am a spirit of no common rate; and I do love thee: therefore go with me. I'll give thee fairies to attend on thee.

She signs to her followers, who obediently attend on Bottom. They all leave the glade, leaving behind the forgotten little Indian boy.

Another part of the wood. Oberon and Puck are together. Puck is helpless with laughter.

PUCK   My mistress with a monster is in love!

OBERON   This falls out better than I could devise. But hast thou yet latched the Athenian's eyes with the love-juice?

24

PUCK   I took him sleeping –

            They are interrupted by the entry of Hermia,
            amorously pursued by Demetrius. Instantly, Puck
            and Oberon become invisible.

OBERON   Stand close; this is the same Athenian.

PUCK   This is the woman, but not this the man.

HERMIA   Out, dog; out, cur! Hast thou slain him then?

DEMETRIUS   I am not guilty of Lysander's blood!

HERMIA   See me no more, whether he be dead or no!

            She flies from him.

DEMETRIUS   There is no following her in this fierce vein . . .

            He sighs and sinks to the ground. He sleeps. Oberon
            and Puck reappear. Oberon remonstrates.

OBERON   What hast thou done? Thou hast mistaken
            quite, and laid the love-juice on some true
            love's sight. About the wood go swifter than the
            wind, and Helena of Athens look thou find!

PUCK   I go, I go, look how I go! Swifter than arrow
            from the Tartar's bow!

With a rush of leaves, as of a sudden wind,
Puck flies off. Oberon bends over the sleeping
Demetrius and anoints his eyes with liquor from
the magic flower.

OBERON   Flower of this purple dye, hit with Cupid's
             archery, sink in th' apple of his eye. When his
             love he doth espy –

Puck returns, mightily out of breath.

PUCK   Captain of our fairy band, Helena is here
             at hand.

Oberon and Puck become invisible as the weeping
Helena, still followed by the ardent Lysander, comes
into the glade. Helena almost falls over the sleeping
Demetrius, who wakes and, seeing her, instantly
falls in love with her.

DEMETRIUS   O Helen, goddess, nymph, perfect, divine!

He tries to embrace her. Alarmed, she backs away
. . . into the waiting arms of Lysander! She cries
out and frees herself. She stares, tearfully, from one
young man to the other.

HELENA   O spite! O hell! I see you are all bent to set
             against me for your merriment! You are both
             rivals, and love Hermia –

26

DEMETRIUS   Lysander, keep thy Hermia! If ere I loved her,
             all that love is Lysander is gone, and now to
             Helen is it home returned!

LYSANDER   Helen, it is not so –

DEMETRIUS   Look where thy love comes; yonder is
             thy dear!

             Enter Hermia. She rushes to Lysander.

HERMIA   Lysander, why unkindly didst thou leave me so?

LYSANDER   (*pushing her away*) Why seek'st thou me? Could
             not this make thee know the hate I bear thee
             made me leave thee so?

HERMIA   Hate me? Wherefore? Am I not Hermia? Are
             not you Lysander?

LYSANDER   Ay, by my life; and never did desire to see thee
             more. Be certain, nothing truer – that I do hate
             thee and love Helena.

             *Hermia stares at Helena, who, flanked by her two
             new lovers, smiles feebly.*

HERMIA   You juggler! You canker-blossom! You thief
             of love!

HELENA   Have you no modesty, no maiden shame? You puppet, you!

HERMIA   Puppet? Thou painted maypole!

She launches herself furiously upon Helena, who skips behind the young men.

HELENA   Let her not hurt me! O, when she is angry, she is keen and shrewd. She was a vixen when she went to school!

HERMIA   Let me come at her!

LYSANDER   Get you gone, you dwarf!

He tries to comfort the terrified Helena. Demetrius pushes him aside. Lysander draws his sword. Demetrius does likewise. They circle each other, and, still threatening, back out of the glade. Hermia and Helena glare at each other.

HERMIA   You, mistress –

HELENA   (*backing away*) Your hands than mine are quicker for a fray; my legs are longer, though, to run away!

She bolts from the glade. Hermia pursues. Oberon and Puck reappear.

28

PUCK   Lord, what fools these mortals be!

OBERON   This is thy negligence; still thou mistak'st, or
             else commits thy knaveries wilfully.

PUCK   Believe me, king of shadows, I mistook.

OBERON   Thou seest these lovers seek a place to fight.
             Hie therefore, Robin, overcast the night . . . and
             lead these testy rivals so astray, as one come not
             within another's way . . . till o'er their brows
             death-counterfeiting sleep with leaden legs and
             batty wings doth creep. (*He gives Puck another
             flower.*) Then crush this herb into Lysander's
             eye . . .

             *As Puck, with magic signs, overcasts the night, a
             thick black fog begins to invade the wood, turning
             the trees to ghosts and the bushes to crouching
             bears. Lysander and Demetrius, no longer able to
             see one another, stumble on, while Puck taunts each
             of the rivals with the other's voice. At last, they
             collapse on the ground, quite overcome with
             weariness. Similarly, Helena and Hermia, pursued
             and pursuer, sink down and fall asleep. Puck, his
             work all but done, bends low over Lysander, and
             crushes the herb upon his eyelids.*

PUCK   When thou wak'st, thou tak'st true delight in
             the sight of thy former lady's eye; and the

country proverb known, that every man should take his own, in your waking shall be shown. Jack shall have Jill, naught shall go ill . . .

Puck gazes at the four sleeping lovers then fades away.

In Titania's glade, the Fairy Queen is entertaining her fantastical love. Donkey-headed Bottom, wreathed in flowers, reclines in Titania's arms, while her attendants gently fan him and tickle his hairy ears. The Indian boy plays on his own.

TITANIA   Sweet love, what desir'st thou to eat?

BOTTOM   Truly, a peck of provender; I could munch dry oats. (*He yawns.*) But I pray you, let none of your people stir me; I have an exposition of sleep come upon me.

TITANIA   Sleep thou, and I will wind thee in my arms. O how I love thee! How I dote on thee!

The attendants steal away as the strange lovers sleep. Oberon appears, with Puck. He looks with pity on the unnatural scene. He sees the Indian boy. He nods to Puck, who bears the child away.

OBERON   Now I have the boy, I will undo this hateful imperfection of her eyes . . . (*He squeezes the herb*

30

into Titania's sleeping eyes.) Be as thou wast wont to be; see as thou wast wont to see . . .

Titania opens her eyes.

TITANIA   My Oberon! what visions have I seen!
           Methought I was enamoured of an ass!

OBERON   There lies your love!

Titania, seeing the sleeping Bottom, shudders. Puck returns. Oberon nods, and Puck restores Bottom to his proper human shape. Titania seems unimpressed by the improvement.

PUCK   Now when thou wak'st, with thine own fool's eyes peep.

OBERON   Come, my queen, take hands with me . . .

Oberon and Titania join hands, and, with Puck and all their returning attendants, dance away. Bottom is left alone, fast asleep and smiling.

Now that the creatures of the night have gone, thin arrows of daylight begin to pierce the wood. There are sounds of hunting horns, and hounds baying. Duke Theseus, with Hippolyta and courtiers, all attired for the hunt, appear.

31

THESEUS	The music of my hounds!
HIPPOLYTA	I was with Hercules and Cadmus once, with hounds of Sparta. I never heard so musical a discord, such sweet thunder.
THESEUS	My hounds are bred out of the Spartan kind; so flew'd, so sanded; and their heads are hung with ears that sweep away the morning dew; slow in pursuit; but matched in mouth like bells, each under each. A cry more tuneable was never hallooed to nor cheered with horn – (*He sees the four lovers, still sleeping.*) But soft, what nymphs are these?

Hermia's father, Egeus, is of the company. Angrily he examines the sleepers.

EGEUS	My lord, this is my daughter here asleep. And this Lysander; this Demetrius is, and this Helena.
THESEUS	Go bid the huntsmen wake them with their horns. (*Obediently, the horns bray out. The lovers awake in some confusion. They see the duke, and at once rise and kneel before him.*) I pray you, all stand up.

They stand, Lysander with Hermia, and Demetrius with Helena. Egeus tries to drag his daughter away

32

from her love. She will not come. Egeus points furiously at Lysander, and addresses the duke.

EGEUS   I beg the law, the law upon his head!

Theseus gazes at the four lovers, and smiles.

THESEUS   Fair lovers, you are fortunately met. Egeus, I will overbear your will; for in the temple, by and by, with us, these couples shall eternally be knit. (*Egeus bows his head and resigns himself to the duke's decree.*) Away with us, to Athens: three and three, we'll hold a feast in great solemnity.

Theseus and his followers leave the glade. The four lovers gaze wonderingly at one another.

DEMETRIUS   These things seem small and indistinguishable, like far-off mountains turned into clouds.

HERMIA   Methinks I see these things with parted eye, when everything seems double.

HELENA   So methinks . . .

DEMETRIUS   Are you sure that we are awake? It seems to me that yet we sleep, we dream. Do not you think the Duke was here?

LYSANDER   And he did bid us follow to the temple.

DEMETRIUS   Why, then, we are awake. Let's follow him, and
            by the way let us recount our dreams.

            *In the glade once inhabited by the Fairy Queen
            lies Bottom, still asleep. Then he, too, awakes, with
            a start.*

BOTTOM   When my cue comes, call me and I will answer.
            My next is, 'most fair Pyramus –' (*He stops and
            stares about him.*) Peter Quince? Flute, the
            bellows-mender? Snout, the tinker? Starveling?
            God's my life! Stolen hence and left me asleep!
            (*He touches his head, and fumbles uneasily for his
            ears. Finding them to be human ears, he sighs with
            relief.*) I have had a most rare vision. (*He gazes
            towards the mossy couch upon which he lay with
            Titania. He smiles.*) I have had a dream . . . I will
            get Peter Quince to write a ballad of this
            dream; it shall be called 'Bottom's Dream',
            because it hath no bottom . . .

            *Back in Athens, in their smoky, candlelit
            room, Peter Quince and his companions are
            sorely distressed.*

QUINCE   Have you sent to Bottom's house?

STARVELING He cannot be heard of.

34

FLUTE   If he come not, the play is marred . . .

QUINCE   You have not a man in all Athens able to
            discharge Pyramus but he.

SNUG   If our sport had gone forward, we had all been
            made men.

FLUTE   O sweet bully Bottom! Thus hath he lost
            sixpence a day during his life. Sixpence a day in
            Pyramus, or nothing.

            *Even as they all mourn the loss of their chief hope,
            their star of stars, the door bursts open and Bottom
            himself stands in the doorway. Panting from
            running, he surveys his fellows, beaming proudly.*

BOTTOM   Where are these lads? Where are these hearts?

QUINCE   Bottom! O most courageous day! O most
            happy hour!

BOTTOM   Get your apparel together! Every man look o'er
            his part; for the short and the long is, our play
            is preferred! Let Thisbe have clean linen, and
            let not him that plays the lion pare his nails.
            And, most dear actors, eat no onions nor garlic,
            for we are to utter sweet breath. No more
            words. Away!

In the royal palace, Theseus and Hippolyta, seated in state and attended by courtiers, await the night's entertainment.

HIPPOLYTA 'Tis strange, my Theseus, that these lovers speak of.

THESEUS More strange than true. The lunatic, the lover, and the poet are of imagination all compact. One sees more devils than vast hell can hold; that is the madman. The lover, all as frantic, sees Helen's beauty in a brow of Egypt. The poet's eye, in a fine frenzy rolling, doth glance from heaven to earth, from earth to heaven, and as imagination bodies forth the forms of things unknown, the poet's pen turns them to shapes, and gives to airy nothing a local habitation and a name. Such tricks hath strong imagination –

HIPPOLYTA But all the story of the night told over, and all their minds transfigured so together, more witnesseth than fancy's images, and grows to something of great constancy; but howsoever, strange and admirable.

The four lovers enter, and Theseus bids them seat themselves and prepare to be entertained. Philostrate, the Master of Revels, steps forward.

PHILOSTRATE A play there is, my lord, some ten words long,

which is as brief as I have known a play; but by ten words, my lord, it is too long.

THESEUS   What are they that do play it?

PHILOSTRATE   Hard-handed men that work in Athens here, which never laboured in their minds till now.

THESEUS   I will hear that play; for never anything can be amiss, when simpleness and duty tender it.

Philostrate bows and withdraws. Presently he ushers in Peter Quince and his company. They are all in costume, even to the man in the moon and the wall.

QUINCE   Gentles, perchance you wonder at this show; but wonder on till truth make all things plain. This man is Pyramus, if you would know; this beauteous lady Thisbe is certain; this man with lime and rough-cast, doth present Wall, that vile wall which did these lovers sunder; this man with lantern, dog and bush of thorn, presenteth Moonshine. This grisly beast, which Lion hight by name . . .

Great applause for the lion. The action of the play commences.

THESEUS   Pyramus draws near the wall; silence!

Bottom, attired as Pyramus, creeps towards Snout, the Wall.

BOTTOM   Thou wall, O wall, O sweet and lovely wall, show me thy chink to blink through with mine eye.

Snout's two fingers are raised for Bottom to blink through.

BOTTOM   No Thisbe do I see! Cursed be thy stones for thus deceiving me!

THESEUS   The wall, methinks, being sensible, should curse again.

BOTTOM   No, in truth sir, he should not. 'Deceiving me' is Thisbe's cue.

Enter Flute, attired as the lady Thisbe.

FLUTE   O wall, full often hast thou heard my moans –

BOTTOM   I see a voice; now will I to the chink, to spy and I can hear my Thisbe's face. Thisbe!

FLUTE   My love!

BOTTOM   Wilt thou at Ninny's tomb meet me straightaway?

FLUTE   Tide life, tide death, I come without delay.

               They exit gracefully.

HIPPOLYTA   This is the silliest stuff that ever I heard.

THESEUS   The best in this kind are but shadows; and
               the worst are no worse, if imagination
               amend them.

               *A tomb has appeared on the stage. Flute enters
               cautiously, accompanied by Moonshine, in the person
               of Starveling with his lantern, bush and dog.*

FLUTE   This is old Ninny's tomb. Where is my love?

               *Enter Snug, as the lion. He roars fiercely. Thisbe
               squeals and flies, dropping her mantle.*

DEMETRIUS   Well roared, lion!

THESEUS   Well run, Thisbe!

               *Lion savages Thisbe's mantle, leaving it bloody,
               then departs.*

THESEUS   Well moused, lion!

               Cheers and applause, and much laughter.

Enter Bottom. He sees the bloody mantle. He exhibits wild despair.

BOTTOM   What dreadful dole is here? Eyes, do you see? How can it be? O dainty duck, O dear! Thy mantle good – What, stained with blood? O Fates, come, come! Come, tears, confound! Out sword, and wound the pap of Pyramus; cry that left pap, where heart doth hop.

He draws his sword and prepares to extinguish himself.

THESEUS   This passion would go near to make a man look sad.

HIPPOLYTA   Beshrew my heart, but I pity the man.

BOTTOM   Thus die I, thus, thus, thus. (*Stabs himself repeatedly, and falls.*) Now am I dead, now am I fled; my soul is in the sky. Moon take thy flight. (*Exit Starveling, with his lantern, bush and dog.*) Now die, die, die, die.

Bottom, with many twitches, jerks, convulsions and groans, dies. Huge applause. Bottom rises, bows in acknowledgement, and lying down, gives an encore of his death agonies. At last, and most reluctantly, he becomes still. Flute enters, and beholds the recumbent Bottom.

40

FLUTE

Asleep, my love? What, dead, my dove? O Pyramus, arise. Speak, speak! Quite dumb? Dead, dead? Come, trusty sword, come blade, my breast imbrue. (*After vainly attempting to wrest the sword from Bottom's death-grasp, Flute stabs himself with the scabbard.*) Thus Thisbe ends – Adieu, adieu, adieu! (*Dies.*)

THESEUS

Moonshine and Lion are left to bury the dead.

DEMETRIUS

Ay, and Wall, too.

Bottom rises.

BOTTOM

No, I assure you, the wall is down that parted their fathers. Will it please you to see the epilogue, or to hear a Bergomask dance?

THESEUS

No epilogue, I pray you; for your play needs no excuse. Never excuse. But come, your Bergomask; let your epilogue alone.

The company bow, and the dance begins. As they dance, the court begins to rise, and, still applauding, the audience drifts away. At last, Bottom and his companions are alone, and at the end of their dance. They look at one another with great satisfaction, shake hands, and depart. Now the great hall is empty and dark. A bell begins to toll midnight. There comes a glimmering of tiny lights;

41

*then Oberon, Titania, Puck and all their fairy
attendants troop in, each holding up a tiny
glowing lamp.*

OBERON Through the house give glimmering light . . .
Sing and dance it trippingly . . .

*The fairies begin to disperse, making strange
patterns with their glowings.*

TITANIA Hand in hand with fairy grace, will we sing and
bless this place.

OBERON Now, until the break of day,
Through this house each fairy stray.
To the best bride-bed will we,
Which by us shall blessed be.

*The fairies repeat the song as they begin to vanish
into the deeper recesses of the palace.*

OBERON Trip away, make no stay; meet me all by break
of day.

*Oberon and Titania vanish in the wake of the
vanishing lights. Puck alone remains. Then he grins
and he too vanishes.*

The curtain falls . . .

Julius Caesar

The Tragedy of Julius Caesar has been called the greatest play about politics ever written. It is a tale of envy, pride and bloated ambition, of treachery and murder. It is the story of four great men and their struggle for power: of Brutus, a good man, who, for what he believes to be the best of reasons, commits the worst of crimes; of Cassius, 'lean and hungry' Cassius, whose love for his friend Brutus causes him to override his own better judgement and so lead his cause to ruin; of Mark Antony, the 'masker and reveller', who is yet the cleverest and most ruthless politician of them all; and it is the story of Julius Caesar himself, a man who has come to believe so much in his own greatness that he thinks himself a god – 'Wilt thou lift up Olympus?' he demands of those who kneel before him to beg for mercy for a friend; and the next instant he perishes under a raging hail of knives . . .

The Characters in the Play

in order of appearance

A SOOTHSAYER

JULIUS CAESAR

CASSIUS   *a conspirator against Julius Caesar*

BRUTUS   *a conspirator against Julius Caesar*

MARK ANTONY   *a general*

CASCA   *a conspirator against Julius Caesar*

CINNA   *a conspirator against Julius Caesar*

LUCIUS   *servant to Brutus*

DEDIUS   *a conspirator against Julius Caesar*

METELLUS   *a conspirator against Julius Caesar*

TREBONIUS   *a conspirator against Julius Caesar*

PORTIA   *wife to Brutus*

CALPHURNIA   *wife to Caesar*

A SENATOR

FOUR PLEBEIANS

CINNA   *the poet*

OCTAVIUS   *a general*

THE GHOST OF CAESAR

PINDARUS   *servant to Cassius*

STRATO   *servant to Brutus*

    Servants, townspeople and soldiers

Julius Caesar

The curtain rises on a great procession through the streets of Rome. The whole city waits to cheer Julius Caesar, ruler of the world, as he returns in triumph from another glorious victory. Calphurnia, his wife, and all the great ones of Rome follow after him like faithful dogs. Suddenly, a voice cries out.

SOOTHSAYER	Caesar!
CAESAR	Speak. Caesar is turned to hear.
SOOTHSAYER	Beware the ides of March.

The soothsayer is brought before Caesar.

CAESAR	What say'st thou to me now? Speak once again.
SOOTHSAYER	Beware the ides of March.
CAESAR	(*staring at the soothsayer*) He is a dreamer. Let us leave him. Pass.

The procession passes on. Brutus and Cassius remain behind. They lean against the plinth of a huge statue of Caesar, which dwarfs them. There are images of Caesar all around.

CASSIUS	Brutus, I have not from your eyes that gentleness and show of love as I was wont to have.

45

BRUTUS	Poor Brutus, with himself at war, forgets the shows of love to other men. (*There is a sound of distant shouting.*) What means this shouting? I do fear the people choose Caesar for their king.
CASSIUS	Ay, do you fear it? Then must I think you would not have it so.
BRUTUS	I would not, Cassius; yet I love him well.

There is another shout.

CASSIUS	Why, man, he doth bestride the narrow world like a Colossus, and we petty men walk under his huge legs, and peep about to find ourselves dishonourable graves. What should be in that 'Caesar'? Why should that name be sounded more than yours?
BRUTUS	Caesar is returning!

Caesar enters, followed by his retinue, which includes his friend Mark Antony. He looks angry, and his followers disturbed.

CAESAR	Antonius!
ANTONY	Caesar?

46

CAESAR Let me have men about me that are fat,
sleek-headed men and such as sleep
a-nights. Yond Cassius has a lean and
hungry look, he thinks too much; such men
are dangerous.

ANTONY Fear him not, Caesar, he's not dangerous.
He is a noble Roman and well given.

CAESAR Would he were fatter! but I fear him not.

*Caesar raises his arm. Trumpets sound, and the
procession continues. Casca stays.*

BRUTUS Casca, tell us what hath chanced today,
that Caesar looks so sad.

CASCA Why, there was a crown offered him. He
put it by; but to my thinking, he would fain
have had it.

CASSIUS Who offered him the crown?

CASCA Mark Antony.

BRUTUS What was the second noise for?

CASCA Why for that too; then he put it by again,
but to my thinking he was very loath to lay
his fingers off it. As he refused it, the

rabblement hooted, and uttered such a
deal of stinking breath, that it had, almost,
choked Caesar, for he fell down at it.

BRUTUS   'Tis very like; he hath the falling sickness.

CASSIUS   No, Caesar hath it not; but you, and I, and
honest Casca, we have the falling sickness.

CASCA   I know not what you mean by that.
Farewell, both.

He goes.

BRUTUS   Tomorrow, if you please to speak with me,
come home to me, and I will wait for you.

CASSIUS   I will do so; till then, think of the world.

Brutus leaves. Cassius is left alone.

CASSIUS   Well, Brutus, thou art noble; yet I see thy
honourable mettle may be wrought; for
who so firm that cannot be seduced?

*A wild night torn by thunder and lightning.
Cassius enters, hastening along a streaming,
glaring street. A shadowy figure meets him. It
is Casca.*

CASSIUS   Who's there?

CASCA   A Roman.

CASSIUS   Casca, by your voice.

CASCA   Cassius, what night is this! Whoever knew
             the heavens menace so?

CASSIUS   Those that have known the earth so full
             of faults.

CASCA   They say the senators tomorrow mean to
             establish Caesar as a king.

CASSIUS   I know where I will wear this dagger then:
             Cassius from bondage will deliver Cassius.

CASCA   So will I. Hold, my hand.

             *They clasp hands. The thunder and lightning
             grow more violent. Cinna enters.*

CASCA   Stand close a while.

CASSIUS   'Tis Cinna. He is a friend. (*The conspirators
             huddle close together.*)

CINNA   O Cassius, if you could but win the noble
             Brutus to our party –

CASSIUS Good Cinna, take this paper, and throw this in at his window. Three parts of him is ours already, and the man entire upon the next encounter yields him ours!

Cinna goes.

Brutus is walking in his orchard. The fury of the heavens has increased and the dark fabric of the sky is ripped apart by comets and shooting stars.

BRUTUS It must be by his death. And for my part I know no personal cause to spurn at him for the general. He would be crowned; how that might change his nature. Crown him? – that – and then I grant we put a sting in him. Therefore think of him as a serpent's egg and kill him in the shell.

His servant Lucius enters.

LUCIUS The taper burneth in your closet, sir. Searching the window for a flint, I found this paper. (*He gives him a scroll.*)

BRUTUS Is not tomorrow, boy, the ides of March?

LUCIUS (*nodding in the affirmative*) Sir, March is wasted fifteen days.

50

There is knocking on the gate.

BRUTUS Go to the gate, somebody knocks.

*Lucius leaves. Brutus opens the scroll
and reads.*

'Brutus, thou sleep'st. Awake and see
thyself! Speak, strike, redress!' Between the
acting of a dreadful thing and the first
motion, all the interim is like a phantasma
or a hideous dream.

*Cassius enters, with Decius, Casca, Cinna,
Metellus and Trebonius. These last are all
cloaked and hooded.*

CASSIUS Good morrow, Brutus.

BRUTUS Know I these men that come along with
you?

CASSIUS Yes, every man of them.

Cassius reveals himself.

BRUTUS Give me your hands all over, one by one.

DECIUS Shall no man else be touched but
only Caesar?

CASSIUS	Decius, well urged. I think it is not meet Mark Antony, so well beloved of Caesar, should outlive Caesar.
BRUTUS	Our course will seem too bloody, to cut the head off and then hack the limbs. Let's be sacrificers, but not butchers, Cassius. And for Mark Antony, think not of him.
CASSIUS	Yet I fear him.
TREBONIUS	Let him not die.
CASSIUS	But it is doubtful yet whether Caesar will come forth today or no, for he is superstitious grown of late.
DECIUS	Never fear that. I can o'ersway him, and I will bring him to the Capitol.
	A clock strikes three.
TREBONIUS	'Tis time to part.
	The conspirators leave. Brutus is left alone. Presently his wife, Portia, comes out of the house and approaches him.
PORTIA	Brutus, my lord!

BRUTUS	Wherefore rise you now?
PORTIA	Dear my lord, make me acquainted with your cause of grief.
BRUTUS	Portia, I am not well in health, and that is all.
PORTIA	No, my Brutus, you have some sick offence within your mind and, upon my knees I charm you, by all your vows of love, that you unfold to me, why you are heavy, and what men tonight have had resort to you, who hid their faces even from the darkness. (*She kneels.*)
BRUTUS	Kneel not, gentle Portia.
PORTIA	I should not need, if you were gentle Brutus. Dwell I but in the suburbs of your good pleasure? If it be no more, Portia is Brutus' harlot, not his wife.
BRUTUS	You are my true and honourable wife, and by and by thy bosom shall partake the secrets of my heart.

It is morning and another wife is filled with fears for her husband. In Caesar's house, Calphurnia pleads with him to stay at home.

CALPHURNIA   What mean you, Caesar? You shall not stir
                out of your house today.

CAESAR   Caesar shall forth.

CALPHURNIA   I never stood on ceremonies, yet now they
                fright me. There is one within recounts
                most horrid sights. A lioness hath whelped
                in the streets, and graves have yawned and
                yielded up their dead; fierce fiery warriors
                fight upon the clouds, which drizzled blood
                upon the Capitol.

CAESAR   These predictions are to the world in
                general as to Caesar.

CALPHURNIA   When beggars die, there are no comets
                seen; the heavens themselves blaze forth
                the death of princes.

CAESAR   Cowards die many times before their
                deaths; the valiant never taste of death
                but once.

CALPHURNIA   Alas, my lord, your wisdom is consumed in
                confidence. Call it my fear that keeps you
                in the house and not your own.

                She kneels. Caesar smiles indulgently.

54

CAESAR   For thy humour, I will stay at home.

                Decius enters.

DECIUS   Caesar, all hail!

CAESAR   Decius, you are come in very happy time to
                bear my greetings to the senators, and tell
                them that I will not come today.

DECIUS   Most mighty Caesar, let me know some cause.

CAESAR   The cause is in my will, I will not come:
                that is enough to satisfy the senate. But
                because I love you I will let you know.
                Calphurnia here, my wife, stays me at
                home. She dreamt tonight she saw my
                statue, which, like a fountain with an
                hundred spouts, did run pure blood, and
                many lusty Romans came smiling and did
                bathe their hands in it.

DECIUS   This dream is all amiss interpreted, it
                signifies that from you great Rome shall
                suck reviving blood.

CAESAR   And this way have you well expounded it.

DECIUS   And know it now: the senate have concluded
                to give this day a crown to mighty Caesar.

If you shall send them word you will not
come, their minds may change.

CAESAR   How foolish do your fears seem now,
Calphurnia! I will go.

*A great crowd awaits outside the Capitol.
There are shouts of 'Caesar! Caesar!' The
shouts increase in volume and excitement. The
faces of the crowd are joyful, eager. Caesar sees
the soothsayer and approaches him, followed by
Brutus, Cassius and the other conspirators.*

CAESAR   The ides of March are come.

SOOTHSAYER   Ay, Caesar, but not gone.

*Caesar shrugs his shoulders, and mounts the
steps into the Capitol. The conspirators follow.
A senator murmurs to Cassius.*

SENATOR   I wish your enterprise today may thrive.

*As he slips away, there is a great amount of
nervous plucking at each other's sleeves and
cloaks. The conspirators mutter to one
another fearfully.*

CASSIUS   I fear our purpose is discovered! Brutus,
what shall be done?

BRUTUS   Cassius, be constant. Popilius Lena speaks
not of our purposes, for look, he smiles,
and Caesar doth not change.

CINNA   Casca, you are the first that rears your
hand.

The conspirators encircle Caesar. Metellus
kneels, then the others. Casca moves behind. As
they kneel, they plead.

METELLUS   Most high, most mighty . . .

CINNA   O Caesar!

CASSIUS   Pardon, Caesar! Caesar, pardon!

Caesar, turning from one supplicant to
another, pulls his clutched gown free.

BRUTUS   I kiss thy hand, but not in flattery, Caesar.

CAESAR   What Brutus?

DECIUS   Great Caesar!

CAESAR   Hence! Wilt thou lift up Olympus?

CASCA   Speak hands for me!

He stabs Caesar in the neck. The others rush upon the staggering Caesar and slash and stab at him. He continues to resist until he sees Brutus.

CAESAR   Et tu, Brute? – (*Seeing Brutus, Caesar covers his face with a gown in pitiful surrender.*) Then fall, Caesar!

Brutus strikes. Caesar dies, and falls at the base of Pompey's statue which has been splattered with blood. There is so much blood from Caesar and the wounded conspirators that it appears to spout blood, as in Calphurnia's dream. There is a moment of terrible silence.

CINNA   Liberty! Freedom! Tyranny is dead!

CASSIUS   Liberty! Freedom!

There is sudden turmoil in the senate, as the senators fly for their lives.

BRUTUS   Fly not, stand still, ambition's debt is paid!

But no one listens, and, presently, the conspirators are alone with their crime.

BRUTUS   Then walk we forth even to the market-

place. Let's all cry, 'Peace, Freedom
and Liberty!'

*As the conspirators kneel and smear their
hands with blood, a shadow falls across them.*

CASSIUS   Where is Mark Antony? (*He appears.*)

BRUTUS   Welcome, Mark Antony.

ANTONY   O mighty Caesar! dost thou lie so low? I
know not, gentlemen, what you intend,
who else must be let blood; if I myself there
is no hour so fit as Caesar's death hour.

BRUTUS   O Antony! Beg not your death of us –

CASSIUS   Your voice shall be as strong as any man's
in the disposing of new dignities.

BRUTUS   Only be patient till we have appeased the
multitude, and then we will deliver you the
cause why I, that did love Caesar when I
struck him, have thus proceeded.

ANTONY   I doubt not of your wisdom. (*He shakes the
conspirators' hands.*) And am, moreover,
suitor that I may produce his body to the
market-place, and in the pulpit, as becomes
a friend, speak in the order of his funeral.

BRUTUS   You shall, Mark Antony.

CASSIUS   (*aside*) You know not what you do. Know you how much the people may be moved by that which he will utter?

BRUTUS   I will myself into the pulpit first, and show the reason of our Caesar's death.

CASSIUS   I know not what may fall; I like it not.

The conspirators leave. There is the roar of a crowd while Brutus speaks.

BRUTUS   Romans, countrymen, and lovers, hear me for my cause.

ANTONY   (*to Caesar's body*) Are all thy conquests, glories, triumphs, spoils, shrunk to this little measure? O pardon me, thou bleeding piece of earth, that I am meek and gentle with these butchers. Woe to the hand that shed this costly blood! (*He pauses.*) Cry havoc, and let slip the dogs of war!

Outside, Brutus addresses the people.

BRUTUS   As Caesar loved me, I weep for him; as he was valiant, I honour him; but, as he was ambitious, I slew him! (*There are loud cheers.*) I have the same dagger for myself, when it shall please my country to need my death!

ALL Live, Brutus! live, live!

1ST PLEBEIAN Bring him with triumph home unto his house!

2ND PLEBEIAN Give him a statue –

3RD PLEBEIAN Let him be Caesar!

Mark Antony enters, bearing Caesar's body. He lays it down on the ground. Brutus leaves.

ANTONY Friends, Romans, countrymen, lend me your ears! I come to bury Caesar, not to praise him. The evil that men do lives after them, the good is oft interred with their bones. So let it be with Caesar. (*During the above, the crowd begins to stir and murmur.*) He was my friend, faithful and just to me; but Brutus says he was ambitious, and Brutus is an honourable man. When that the poor have cried, Caesar hath wept; ambition should be made of sterner stuff; yet Brutus says he was ambitious, and Brutus is an honourable man. You all did see I thrice presented him a kingly crown, which he did thrice refuse. Was this ambition?

1ST PLEBEIAN	Methinks there is much reason in his sayings.
2ND PLEBEIAN	Caesar has had great wrong.
3RD PLEBEIAN	I fear there will a worse come in his place.
4TH PLEBEIAN	There's not a nobler man in Rome than Antony!

The crowd begins to surge. The cry of 'Antony! Antony! Antony!' goes up.

ANTONY	If you have tears, prepare to shed them now. Look, in this place ran Cassius' dagger through; see what a rent the envious Casca made.
1ST PLEBEIAN	O piteous spectacle!
2ND PLEBEIAN	O noble Caesar!
ANTONY	Through this the well-beloved Brutus stabbed. This was the most unkindest cut of all.
4TH PLEBEIAN	O traitors, villains!

2ND PLEBEIAN   We will be revenged!

ALL   Revenge! Seek! Burn! Fire! Kill! Let not a
                 traitor live!

                 *The crowd, like a river in full spate, now bursts
                 its banks and rushes through the streets,
                 tearing up benches, and anything that comes in
                 its way, shouting –*

ALL   Away, away! Revenge, revenge!

                 *They seize on a poor, unfortunate man. He
                 struggles to be free.*

CINNA THE POET   I am Cinna the poet! I am Cinna the poet!
                 I am not Cinna the conspirator!

                 Cinna is dragged away, screaming.

ANTONY   (*watching the riot with grim satisfaction*) Now
                 let it work. Mischief, thou art afoot, take
                 thou what course thou wilt.

                 *The conspirators flee from the fury of the
                 people. Anyone against whom there is the
                 smallest suspicion is ruthlessly put to death by
                 order of Mark Antony and young Octavius,
                 Caesar's nephew and heir to his name. Brutus
                 and Cassius escape into Asia where they raise*

*armies to march against Antony and Octavius.
But all is not well between the friends: Brutus
accuses Cassius of taking bribes.*

*Outside Brutus' tent, officers are listening,
frowning and worried. Within the tent, Brutus
and Cassius confront one another. Both are
dressed for battle. Cassius looks the more
seasoned and professional.*

CASSIUS   I – an itching palm! When Caesar lived, he
             durst not thus have moved me.

BRUTUS   You durst not so have tempted him. (*With
             clenched fists*) Remember March, the ides of
             March remember. Did not great Julius
             bleed for justice's sake?

CASSIUS   Do not presume too much upon my love, I
             may do that I shall be sorry for.

BRUTUS   You have done that you should be
             sorry for.

CASSIUS   You love me not.

BRUTUS   I do not like your faults.

CASSIUS   A friendly eye could never see such faults.

BRUTUS   O Cassius, I am sick of many griefs. Portia
              is dead.

CASSIUS   How 'scaped I killing when I crossed you
              so? Upon what sickness?

BRUTUS   Impatient of my absence, and grief that
              young Octavius with Mark Antony have
              made themselves so strong; with this she
              fell distract and swallowed fire.

CASSIUS   Portia, art thou gone?

BRUTUS   No more, I pray you. I have here received
              letters that young Octavious and Mark
              Antony come down upon us with a mighty
              power. What think you of marching to
              Philippi presently?

CASSIUS   I do not think it good.

BRUTUS   Our cause is ripe. The enemy increaseth
              every day; we, at the height, are ready to
              decline. There is a tide in the affairs of
              men, which taken at the flood, leads on to
              fortune. And we must take the current
              when it serves.

CASSIUS   Then with your will, go on; we'll along
              ourselves, and meet them at Philippi.

Cassius leaves Brutus. The page, Lucius, is fast asleep in a corner. Brutus gently covers him and seats himself at his table. The yellow flame flickers, then begins to burn blue.

The ghost of Caesar enters.

BRUTUS   Ha! Who comes here? Art thou any thing? Speak to me what thou art!

GHOST   Thy evil spirit, Brutus.

BRUTUS   Why com'st thou?

GHOST   To tell thee thou shalt see me at Philippi.

BRUTUS   Well: then I shall see thee again?

GHOST   Ay.

The ghost vanishes.

On the plain of Philippi, Octavius and Mark Antony await the coming battle. Their great army stretches behind them. In the distance there is a faint glimmer of the enemy's steel.

ANTONY   Octavius, lead your battle softly on upon the left hand of the even field.

OCTAVIUS   Upon the right hand, I. Keep thou the left.

ANTONY   Why do you cross me?

OCTAVIUS   I do not cross you, but I will do so.

                Octavius and Antony return to their lines.
                Cassius confers with an officer.

CASSIUS   (*very sadly to an officer*) This is my birthday;
                as this very day was Cassius born. Be thou
                witness that against my will am I
                compelled to set upon one battle all our
                liberties. (*Brutus joins him.*) Now, most
                noble Brutus, if we lose this battle, are you
                contented to be led in triumph through the
                streets of Rome?

BRUTUS   No, Cassius, no. But this same day must
                end that work the ides of March begun.
                And whether we shall meet again I know
                not; for ever, and for ever, farewell,
                Cassius! If we do meet again, why, we shall
                smile; if not, why then this parting was
                well made.

CASSIUS   For ever, and for ever, farewell, Brutus! If
                we do meet again, we'll smile indeed; if
                not, 'tis true this parting was well made.

They ride away, together at first, then parting, one to the left, the other right.

The legions march towards one another. Then comes the clash of their meeting. There is violent fighting. The world is full of blood and dust, and the sounds of screams and howls, and blazing trumpets. All day long the battle raged. At last, the sun went down at Philippi. Antony and Octavius were victorious.

PINDARUS   Fly further off my lord. Mark Antony is in your tents.

CASSIUS   This day I breathed first; this is come round, and where I did begin, there shall I end. Caesar, thou art reveng'd, even with the sword that kill'd thee.

The battlefield darkens. Brutus bends over the dead body of Cassius who has killed himself rather than be captured.

The ghost of Caesar appears briefly and then fades away.

BRUTUS   O Julius Caesar, thou art mighty yet. (*He stares down.*) The last of all the Romans, fare thee well! Friends, I owe more tears to this dead man than you shall see me pay. I shall find time, Cassius, I shall find time. (*They all sit down.*) Our enemies have beat us to the pit. It is more worthy to leap in ourselves than tarry till they push us.

There are shouts in the distance and the approach of glimmering torches. Brutus bids farewell to his friends, all of whom leave save one, an old soldier by name of Strato.

BRUTUS I know my hour is come. (*He runs on his sword.*) Caesar, now be still, I killed not thee with half so good a will.

He dies. The torches draw near.

The victorious Romans, Antony and Octavius, come upon the dead body of Brutus with Strato guarding it.

ANTONY How died thy master, Strato?

STRATO Brutus only overcame himself, and no man else hath honour by his death.

ANTONY (*to Brutus*) This was the noblest Roman of them all: all the conspirators, save only he, did that they did in envy of great Caesar. He only, in a general honest thought and common good to all, made one of them.

His life was gentle, and the elements so
mixed in him that Nature might stand up
and say to all the world, 'This was a man'.

The curtain falls.

Twelfth Night

'What country, my friends, is this?' asks a young woman on a strange sea-shore; and the answer comes: 'This is Illyria, lady.' And so the story begins.

Illyria: land of a lovesick duke, a countess in deep mourning, her drunken uncle and his rowdy friends, and a solemn steward with a face as long as Sunday, who thinks, because he is virtuous, there should be no more cakes and ale. Then, into this world, comes a pair of shipwrecked twins to wreak havoc among hearts and heads; and through it all, like a vein of dancing quicksilver, run the songs and wit of Feste, the jester, the wisest fool in the land: for he is paid to play the fool, while the rest of Illyria does it for nothing.

Shakespeare wrote the play when he was about thirty-seven, just after the tragic *Hamlet* and just before the bitter *Troilus and Cressida*; though all it has in common with its stern neighbours is the genius of its creator.

The title refers to an ancient Festival of Fools, a time of carnival, when everything is turned upside down, when blindfold love blunders in a circle, forever missing his mark.

Shakespeare gave the play an alternative title: *What You Will*, as if to offer the audience its own choice. King Charles I liked to call it *Malvolio*, after his favourite character; but the play is so rich in favourites, that the world has decided not to meddle in choices, and leave it at *Twelfth Night*.

The Characters in the Play

in order of appearance

ORSINO	*Duke of Illyria*
SIR TOBY BELCH	*Olivia's kinsman*
MARIA	*Olivia's waiting-gentlewoman*
SIR ANDREW AGUECHEEK	*Sir Toby's companion*
VIOLA	*later disguised as Cesario*
CAPTAIN	*of the wrecked ship, befriending Viola*
COURTIER	
LUTE PLAYER	
OLIVIA	*a countess*
FESTE	*jester to Olivia*
MALVOLIO	*Olivia's steward*
SEBASTIAN	*Viola's twin brother*
ANTONIO	*a sea-captain, befriending Sebastian*
SERVANT	*of Olivia*
OFFICER	*in the service of the Duke*
PRIEST	

The curtain rises on a wild sea upon which a fragile vessel is being tossed to and fro. Tremendous waves pound its sides as if to smash it like an egg-shell; and tiny figures fling themselves over the sides and strike out desperately for land.

Beyond its wild sea coast, Illyria is a green and pleasant land, ruled over by the Duke Orsino, a gentleman made melancholy by unrequited love . . .

In the duke's mansion, he sits, listening to the sad music of a lute-player. Presently the music ceases.

DUKE   If music be the food of love, play on, give me excess of it . . .

As the lute-player resumes, the duke rises and goes to a window and gazes out towards a distant mansion. He sighs, for within that mansion is his love. She is the Countess Olivia, and she will have nothing to do with him.

In Olivia's house, all is sober and hung with black, for she is in mourning for a dead brother and has vowed to admit no thoughts of love for seven long years. But though all is mournful above stairs, in the wine cellar, like a stormy stomach below a calm face, riot ferments and bubbles in the person of her boozy uncle, Sir Toby Belch. He is with Maria, the countess's pretty waiting-woman.

SIR TOBY   What a plague means my niece to take the

74

death of her brother thus? I am sure care's an
enemy to life.

MARIA   By my troth, Sir Toby, you must come in earlier
a'nights. Your cousin, my lady, takes great
exception to your ill hours.

SIR TOBY   Why, let her except before excepted.
(*He drinks.*)

MARIA   That quaffing and drinking will undo you: I
heard my lady talk of it yesterday; and of a
foolish knight that you brought in one night to
be her wooer.

SIR TOBY   Who, Sir Andrew Aguecheek?

MARIA   Ay, he.

SIR TOBY   He's as tall as any man in Illyria!

MARIA   What's that to th'purpose?

SIR TOBY   Why, he has three thousand ducats a year.

MARIA   He's a very fool and a prodigal. He's drunk
nightly in your company!

SIR TOBY   With drinking healths to my niece! I'll drink to
her as long as there is a passage in my throat,

and drink in Illyria! Here comes Sir Andrew Agueface!

Enter Sir Andrew Aguecheek, a tall, thin, fair-haired gentleman. He bows gallantly to Maria.

SIR ANDREW   Bless you, fair shrew!

MARIA   And you too, sir.

SIR ANDREW   Shall we not set about some revels?

SIR TOBY   What else shall we do? (*Gives Sir Andrew a drink.*) Let me see thee caper! (*Sir Andrew drinks and begins to dance, somewhat wildly.*) Ha, higher, higher!

Sir Toby joins in the dance and the two gentlemen clutch at Maria, who, helpless with laughter, evades them and makes her escape.

The sea-shore. A storm-battered boat lies on the beach and, beside it, some half dozen survivors from the shipwreck: among them is a young woman, Viola.

VIOLA   What country, friends, is this?

CAPTAIN   This is Illyria, lady.

VIOLA   And what should I do in Illyria? My brother, he

is in Elysium. (*She gazes sadly out to sea.*)
Perchance he is not drowned: what think
you, sailors?

CAPTAIN   It is perchance that you yourself were saved.

VIOLA   O my poor brother! and so perchance may he be!

CAPTAIN   True, madam, and to comfort you with chance,
assure yourself – After our ship did split, I
saw your brother bind himself to a strong
mast that lived upon the sea. I saw him hold
acquaintance with the waves so long as I
could see.

VIOLA   For saying so, there's gold! Knowest thou
this country?

CAPTAIN   Ay, madam.

VIOLA   Who governs here?

CAPTAIN   Orsino.

VIOLA   Orsino! I have heard my father name him. I'll
serve this duke. Thou shalt present me as an
eunuch to him . . .

*The captain nods, and Viola clasps him gratefully
by the hand.*

So Viola, with the captain's help, becomes Cesario, a page, and attired as a man, serves the duke in his palace.

COURTIER   If the duke continues these favours towards you, Cesario, you are like to be much advanced; he hath known you but three days and already you are no stranger.

The duke enters. Viola gazes at him, and it is evident that her feelings towards him are somewhat stronger than those of a page for his master.

DUKE   Cesario, thou knowest no less but all: I have unclasped to thee the book even of my secret soul. (*He goes to the window and gazes towards the mansion of Olivia.*) Therefore, good youth, address thy gait unto her, be not denied access, stand at her doors, and tell them, there thy fixed foot shall grow till thou have audience.

VIOLA   Say I do speak with her, my lord, what then?

DUKE   O then unfold the passion of my love.

VIOLA   I'll do my best to woo your lady. (*She takes her departure, glancing back at the lovesick duke.*) Yet . . . whoe'er I woo, myself would be his wife!

As Viola departs, the duke signs to his lute-player, who sings:

78

LUTE-PLAYER   Come away, come away death,
               And in sad cypress let me be laid.
               Fly away, fly away breath,
               I am slain by a fair cruel maid . . .

               *The fair cruel maid is Olivia in her mansion, all
               in black. She is attended by solemn servants,
               and Feste, her jester, who tries, vainly, to make
               her smile.*

OLIVIA   Take the fool away.

FESTE   Do you not hear, fellows? Take away the lady.

OLIVIA   Sir, I bade them take away you.

FESTE   Misprision in the highest degree! Good
               madonna, give me leave to prove you a fool.

OLIVIA   Can you do it?

FESTE   Dexteriously, madam. Good madonna, why
               mourn'st thou?

OLIVIA   Good fool, for my brother's death.

FESTE   I think his soul is in hell, madonna.

OLIVIA   I know his soul is in heaven, fool.

FESTE   The more fool, madonna, to mourn for your
               brother's soul, being in heaven. Take away the
               fool, gentlemen!

               *Maria enters with Olivia's steward, Malvolio, a
               solemn, long-faced personage, who looks exceedingly
               disapprovingly at the jester.*

MARIA   Madam, there is at the gate a young gentleman
               much desires to speak with you.

OLIVIA   Tell him he shall not speak with me.

MALVOLIO   He has been told so; and says he'll stand at
               your door like a sheriff's post . . .

OLIVIA   What manner of man?

MALVOLIO   Of very ill manner: he'll speak with you, will
               you or no.

OLIVIA   Of what personage and years is he?

MALVOLIO   Not yet old enough for a man, nor young
               enough for a boy; as a squash is before 'tis a
               peascod. 'Tis with him in standing water,
               between boy and man.

OLIVIA   (*wearily*) Let him approach. (*Malvolio departs.
               Olivia turns to her maid, Maria.*) Give me my

veil: come, throw it o'er my face. We'll once
more hear Orsino's embassy.

*Maria veils her mistress's face, and, with other
black-gowned ladies of Olivia's court, stands behind
her. Viola enters with a gallant flourish of her
plumed cap. She is every inch the gentleman, and,
one might say, with inches over and to spare.*

VIOLA   The honourable lady of the house, which
        is she?

OLIVIA Speak to me. I shall answer for her.

VIOLA   Most radiant, exquisite and unmatchable
        beauty – I pray you tell me if this be the lady
        of the house, for I never saw her. I would be
        loath to cast away my speech. Are you the lady
        of the house?

OLIVIA I am. Speak your office.

VIOLA   It alone concerns your ear.

        Olivia gazes at the 'young man' thoughtfully.

OLIVIA Give us this place alone. (*The attendants depart.*)
        Now sir, what is your text?

VIOLA   In Orsino's bosom.

OLIVIA   O, I have read it: it is heresy. Have you no more to say?

Viola stares curiously at the veiled face before her.

VIOLA   Good madam, let me see your face.

OLIVIA   Have you any commission from your lord to negotiate with my face? You are now out of your text; but we will draw the curtain, and show you the picture. (*She draws aside her veil.*) Is't not well done?

VIOLA   Excellently done, if God did all.

OLIVIA   'Tis in grain, sir, 'twill endure wind and weather.

VIOLA   'Tis beauty truly blent. Lady, you are the cruell'st she alive if you would lead these graces to the grave and leave the world no copy. My lord and master loves you. If I did love you in my master's flame, in your denial I would find no sense; I would not understand it.

OLIVIA   Why, what would you?

VIOLA   Make me a willow cabin at your gate, and call upon my soul within the house; write loyal cantons of contemèd love, and sing them loud even in the dead of night; halloo your name to

the reverberate hills, and make the babbling
gossip of the air cry out 'Olivia!' O, you should
not rest between the elements of earth and air
but you should pity me!

OLIVIA   You might do much. What is your parentage?

VIOLA   Above my fortunes.

OLIVIA   Get you to your lord: I cannot love him: let him
send no more, unless, perchance, you come to
me again . . .

VIOLA   (*bowing her way out*) Farewell, fair cruelty!

*Olivia gazes after the departed 'young man'. She
sighs, and her eyes are filled with a sudden
tenderness.*

OLIVIA   What is your parentage? Above my fortunes.
(*She sighs again*). Malvolio!

*The gloomy steward enters. Olivia beckons him
close and murmurs to him.*

*Viola, her embassy completed as unsuccessfully as
she could have wished, strides along the road
towards the duke's palace. But she is being followed.
Malvolio, his black coat flapping and his skinny
black legs twinkling, hastens to overtake her.*

MALVOLIO   Were you not even now with the Countess
             Olivia?

VIOLA   Even now, sir.

MALVOLIO   She returns this ring to you, sir. (*Disdainfully he
             holds out a ring to her. Viola stares at it, bewildered.
             Malvolio shrugs his shoulders, and drops it on the
             ground.*) If it be worth stooping for, there it lies:
             if not, be it his that finds it. (*He stalks away.
             Viola picks up the ring.*)

VIOLA   I left no ring with her: what means this lady?
             (*She is suddenly alarmed.*) She loves me, sure!
             Poor lady, she were better love a dream!

             *In the wine-cellar of the Countess's house, Feste,
             her fool, is singing to Sir Toby and Sir Andrew,
             while round about, like music-charmed monsters,
             great barrels and bottles wink and sway in
             the candlelight.*

FESTE   O mistress mine, where are you roaming?
             O stay and hear, your true love's coming,
             That can sing both high and low.
             Trip no further, pretty sweeting;
             Journeys end in lovers meeting,
             Every wise man's son doth know . . .

SIR ANDREW   A mellifluous voice, as I am a true knight.

SIR TOBY   But shall we make the welkin dance indeed?

SIR ANDREW   Let's do it! Come, begin!

They begin to sing a round, with much banging of tankards on the table. Maria enters, in her night attire.

MARIA   What a caterwauling do you keep here! (*Sir Toby catches her round the waist and, despite her protests, whirls her off in a drunken dance. The uproar continues. Malvolio enters, grim as death at a wedding.*)

MALVOLIO   My masters, are you mad? Have you no wit, manners nor honesty but to gabble like tinkers at this time of night?

The dance comes to a panting conclusion.

SIR TOBY   Dost thou think because thou art virtuous there shall be no more cakes and ale?

MALVOLIO   (*grimly*) She shall know of it. (*He points meaningly upward, and stalks away.*)

MARIA   Go shake your ears. (*She shakes her fist after the pompous steward.*) For Monsieur Malvolio, let me alone with him! If I do not gull him, do not think I have wit enough to lie straight in my bed: I know I can do it!

85

SIR TOBY   What wilt thou do?

MARIA   I will drop in his way some obscure epistles of
            love. I can write very like my lady, your niece –

SIR TOBY   Excellent, I smell a device!

SIR ANDREW I have it in my nose too!

SIR TOBY   He shall think by the letters that thou wilt drop
            that they come from my niece, and that she's in
            love with him.

MARIA   My purpose is indeed a horse of that colour.

            Maria departs.

SIR TOBY   Let's to bed, knight. Thou hadst need send for
            more money.

SIR ANDREW If I cannot recover your niece, I am a foul
            way out.

SIR TOBY   Send for money, knight; if thou hast her not i'
            the end, call me cut.

            *In Orsino's palace, the duke has received the
            unhappy news of the failure of his embassy. Viola
            stands in attendance.*

DUKE   Once more, Cesario, get thee to yon same
        sovereign cruelty. Tell her my love . . .

VIOLA   But if she cannot love you?

DUKE   I cannot be so answered.

VIOLA   Sooth, but you must. Say that some lady, as
        perhaps there is, hath for your love as great a
        pang of heart as you have for Olivia –

DUKE   – Make no compare between that love a woman
        can bear me, and that I owe Olivia!

VIOLA   Ay, but I know –

DUKE   What dost thou know?

VIOLA   Too well what love women to men may owe.
        My father had a daughter loved a man as it
        might be, perhaps, were I a woman, I should
        your lordship.

DUKE   And what's her history?

VIOLA   A blank, my lord. She never told her love, but
        let concealment, like a worm i' the bud, feed on
        her damask cheek; she pined in thought, and
        with a green and yellow melancholy she sat like

Patience on a monument, smiling at grief. Was
not this love indeed?

DUKE But died thy sister of her love, my boy?

VIOLA I am all the daughters of my father's house, and
all the brothers, too – and yet I know not. Sir,
shall I to this lady?

Orsino nods.

*The garden of Olivia's mansion. It is a maze of
intersecting paths and high box hedges. Like witty
insects of the larger sort, Sir Toby, Sir Andrew and
Maria scurry hither and thither and, finding a
suitable path, drop a letter upon it. Then they
vanish behind the hedges. Presently, solemn as an
aged beetle, Malvolio comes strolling along. As he
walks, he muses, and reveals to the unseen watchers,
his secret self.*

MALVOLIO 'Tis but fortune, all is fortune. Maria once told
me she did affect me . . . To be Count
Malvolio! There's an example for it: the Lady of
the Strachy married the yeoman of the
wardrobe. Having been three months married
to her, sitting in my state – (*He sees the letter.
He frowns, then glancing cautiously about him,
bends and picks it up. He studies it.*) By my life,
this is my lady's hand! 'To the unknown

beloved.' To whom should this be? (*He breaks the seal and begins to read.*) 'Jove knows I love, but who? Lips do not move: no man must know. M.O.A.I. doth sway my life.' M.O.A.I. Every one of these letters are in my name! 'If this fall into thy hand, revolve.' (*He revolves.*) 'In my stars I am above thee, but be not afraid of greatness. Some are born great, some achieve greatness, some have greatness thrust upon 'em. Thy fates open their hands. Remember who commended thy yellow stockings and wished to see thee ever cross-gartered: I say, remember. Go to, thou art made if thou desirest to be so; if not, let me see thee steward still.' This is open! 'Thou canst not choose to know who I am. If thou entertain'st my love, let it appear in thy smiling. Thy smiles become thee well.' Jove, I thank thee! I will smile; I will do everything that thou wilt have me!

Malvolio, overwhelmed by his good fortune, skips and capers away. The conspirators emerge from concealment, shaking with laughter and delight at the success of their plot. Maria and Sir Toby make off; Sir Andrew lingers, for he has seen that Olivia, attended by a lady, approaches. Sir Andrew steps forward and executes a courtly bow. Olivia ignores him, for she has seen Viola approaching.

VIOLA   (*bowing*) Most excellent accomplished lady, the heavens rain odours on you!

               Sir Andrew backs away and secretes himself behind a hedge.

SIR ANDREW   That youth's a rare courtier – 'rain odours' – well!

               Olivia dismisses her companion and sits upon a rustic bench.

OLIVIA   Give me your hand, sir.

VIOLA   My duty, madam, and most humble service. (*Offers a hand Olivia seizes it and pulls Viola to sit beside her.*) Dear lady –

OLIVIA   Give me leave, beseech you. What is your name?

VIOLA   Cesario is your servant's name, fair princess.

OLIVIA   My servant, sir? Y'are servant to the Count Orsino, youth.

VIOLA   Madam, I come to whet your gentle thoughts on his behalf –

OLIVIA   I bade you never speak of him again –

VIOLA   You'll nothing, madam, to my lord, by me? (*She tries to escape.*)

OLIVIA   Stay! Cesario, by the roses of the spring, by maidenhood, honour, truth and everything, I love thee –

VIOLA   (*at last escaping from Olivia's loving clutches*) Adieu, good madam; never more will I my master's tears to you deplore!

OLIVIA   Yet come again!

She holds out her arms to the fast vanishing Viola.

In the wine-cellar of Olivia's mansion, Sir Toby and Maria are together. They are joined by a bewildered and hurt Sir Andrew.

SIR ANDREW   I saw your niece do more favours to the count's servingman than ever she bestowed on me!

SIR TOBY   Why then, challenge me the count's youth to fight with him, hurt him in eleven places. There is no love-maker in the world can more prevail in man's commendation with women than report of valour!

MARIA   There is no way but this, Sir Andrew.

They look at one another. Sir Andrew draws his sword and flourishes it. He will take the good advice, and challenge the youth to a duel.

In the town, a perfect image of Viola is walking with a gentleman. It is Sebastian, her twin brother, who, like herself, has been saved from the sea.

SEBASTIAN You must know of me then, Antonio, my name is Sebastian. Some hour before you took me from the breach of the sea was my sister drowned.

ANTONIO Alas, the day!

SEBASTIAN What's to do? Shall we go see the relics of this town?

ANTONIO Would you'd pardon me. I do not without danger walk these streets. Once in a sea- fight 'gainst the Count his galleys, I did some service. If I be lapsed in this place I shall pay dear.

SEBASTIAN Do not walk then too open.

ANTONIO It doth not fit me. Hold, sir, here's my purse. In the south suburbs, at the Elephant, is best to lodge. (*He offers his purse to Sebastian.*)

SEBASTIAN   Why I your purse?

ANTONIO   Haply your eye shall light upon some toy you have desire to purchase.

SEBASTIAN   I'll be your purse-bearer and leave you for an hour . . .

They part.

In Olivia's mansion, the lady is seated with Maria.

OLIVIA   Where's Malvolio? He is sad and civil, and suits well for a servant with my fortunes. Where is Malvolio?

MARIA   (*going to the door*) He is coming, madam, but in a very strange manner.

Malvolio enters. He is solemnly black above, but riotously yellow below; and his skinny legs are imprisoned in black cross-gartering, like starved canaries in a cage. He is smiling with great determination.

OLIVIA   (*amazed*) How now, Malvolio?

MALVOLIO   (*roguishly*) Sweet lady, ho, ho!

OLIVIA   Smil'st thou? I sent for thee upon a sad occasion.

MALVOLIO   Sad, lady? I could be sad. (*He tries to loosen his garters.*) This does make some obstruction in the blood, this cross-gartering. But what of that?

OLIVIA   What is the matter with thee? Wilt thou go to bed, Malvolio?

MALVOLIO   (*reacting with surprise and delight*) To bed? Ay, sweetheart and I'll come to thee!

OLIVIA   What mean'st thou by that, Malvolio?

MALVOLIO   Some are born great –

OLIVIA   Ha?

MALVOLIO   Some achieve greatness –

OLIVIA   What say'st thou?

MALVOLIO   And some have greatness thrust upon them! (*He attempts to embrace Olivia who reacts with horror.*)

OLIVIA   Heavens restore thee! This is very midsummer madness!

A servant enters.

SERVANT   Madam, the young gentleman of the Count
Orsino's is returned –

OLIVIA   I'll come to him. (*To Maria*) Good Maria, let
this fellow be looked to. Let some of my people
have a special care of him.

*Exit Olivia. Sir Toby's inflamed face appears round
the door, followed by the portly rest of him.*

MALVOLIO   Go hang yourselves all; you are idle, shallow
things, I am not of your element.

*He stalks away. Sir Toby and Maria look at one
another happily.*

SIR TOBY   Come, we'll have him in a dark room and
bound. My niece is already in the belief
he's mad . . .

*At the gate of the mansion where Olivia has
hastened to meet Viola, and to renew her
protestations of love. They have not been
well received.*

OLIVIA   I have said too much unto a heart of stone.

VIOLA   With the same haviour that your passion bears
goes on my master's grief.

OLIVIA   Here, wear this jewel for me, 'tis my
          picture. Refuse it not, it hath no tongue
          to vex you. What shall you ask of me that
          I'll deny?

VIOLA   Nothing but this: your true love for my master.

OLIVIA   How with mine honour may I give him that
          which I have given to you?

VIOLA   (*departing*) I will acquit you.

OLIVIA   Well, come again tomorrow. Fare thee well.

          *Olivia retires. Viola begins to walk away, but is
          accosted by Sir Toby and Feste, the jester.*

SIR TOBY Gentleman, God save thee.

VIOLA   And you, sir.

SIR TOBY That defence thou hast, betake thee to it. (*He
          points to Viola's sword.*)

VIOLA   (*uneasily*) You mistake, sir: I am sure no man
          hath any quarrel with me.

SIR TOBY You'll find it otherwise, I assure you. Therefore,
          if you hold your life at any price, betake you to
          your guard: for your opposite has in him what

youth, strength, skill and wrath, can furnish a
man withal.

VIOLA   I pray you, sir, what is he?

SIR TOBY   He is a knight. Souls and bodies hath he
             divorced three.

VIOLA   (*trembling*) I will return again into the house. I
             am no fighter.

SIR TOBY   Sir, no. (*He bars Viola's way.*)

VIOLA   I beseech you, do me this courteous office,
             as to know of the knight what my offence to
             him is.

SIR TOBY   I will do so. (*He turns to Feste*) Stay by this
             gentleman till my return.

             *Sir Toby departs. Viola eyes Feste. She tries to
             make off. Deftly, Feste dances in front of her. There
             is no escape.*

VIOLA   I beseech you, what manner of man is he?

FESTE   He is indeed, sir, the most skilful, bloody and
             fatal opposite that you could possibly have
             found in any part of Illyria.

While Feste is preparing Viola for the worst outside the gate, within it, Sir Toby is performing the same office for the petrified Sir Andrew.

SIR TOBY   Why, man, he is a very devil, I have not seen such a firago. They say he has been fencer to the Sophy.

SIR ANDREW   Pox on't, I'll not meddle with him!

SIR TOBY   Ay, but he will not now be pacified.

Sir Andrew tries to make off, but Sir Toby holds him fast. Outside the gate, Feste is likewise holding Viola. The gate is opened and the two combatants are thrust towards one another.

VIOLA   Pray God defend me! A little thing would make me tell them how much I lack of a man!

SIR TOBY   Come, Sir Andrew, there's no remedy.

VIOLA   I do assure you, 'tis against my will!

Viola and Sir Andrew draw swords and, with faces averted, advance towards one another. But before their blades can touch, they are interrupted. Antonio appears. Instantly, he draws his own sword and parts the duelists.

ANTONIO   Put up your sword! If this young gentleman
have done offence, I'll take the fault on me!

*There is general amazement; but before it can be
resolved, officers come upon the scene and instantly
seize Antonio.*

OFFICER   Antonio, I arrest thee at the suit of
Count Orsino!

ANTONIO   I must obey. (*To Viola*) This comes with seeking
you. Now my necessity makes me to ask you for
my purse.

Viola stares at him blankly.

OFFICER   Come, sir, away.

ANTONIO   I must entreat you for some of that money.

VIOLA   What money, sir?

ANTONIO   Will you deny me now? Is't possible that my
deserts to you can lack persuasion?

VIOLA   I know of none, nor know I you by voice or
any feature.

ANTONIO   O heavens themselves!

99

OFFICER   Come sir, I pray you go.

ANTONIO   This youth that you see here I snatched one
              half out of the jaws of death –

OFFICER   What's that to us? The time goes by. Away!

ANTONIO   O how vile an idol proves this god!
              Thou hast, Sebastian, done good
              feature shame.

OFFICER   The man grows mad. Away with him! Come,
              come, sir.

              (*Antonio is led away.*)

VIOLA   He named Sebastian! O if it prove, tempests are
              kind and salt waves fresh in love!

              Before Sir Toby can stop her, she runs away.

SIR TOBY   A very dishonest paltry boy, and more coward
              than hare.

SIR ANDREW   I'll after him again, and beat him!

              *They are about to set off when, to their great
              surprise, their quarry approaches from the opposite
              direction. It is Sebastian.*

100

SIR ANDREW	(*fiercely*) Now sir, have I met you again? There's for you!

He strikes at Sebastian with his sword. Sebastian, astonished and outraged to find himself so unreasonably set upon, returns the blow with interest.

SEBASTIAN	Why there's for thee, and there, and there!
SIR TOBY	Come on, sir, hold! (*He attempts to intervene.*)
SEBASTIAN	What wouldst thou now? Draw thy sword!

Sir Toby draws; however, at the first clash of steel, Olivia appears.

OLIVIA	Hold, Toby! on thy life, I charge thee, hold!

The combatants part.

SIR TOBY	(*contritely*) Madam!
OLIVIA	Ungracious wretch! Out of my sight! (*Sir Toby, Sir Andrew and Feste hastily depart. Olivia turns to Sebastian.*) I prithee, gentle friend, go with me to my house. (*Sebastian stands and gapes. Olivia takes him by the hand and draws him within the gate.*) Thou shalt not choose but go. Do not deny . . .

Sebastian, dazedly, suffers himself to be led by the lovely Olivia.

SEBASTIAN   If it be thus to dream, still let me sleep.

They go into the mansion.

Even as Sebastian is in a dream of heaven, Malvolio is in a dream of hell. He has been confined, as a madman, in a dark room with a barred door. Feste, in the guise of a priest, one Sir Topaz, visits him, while Sir Toby and Maria listen eagerly to what passes, as Feste and Malvolio converse through the bars.

MALVOLIO   Do not think I am mad! They have laid me here in hideous darkness!

FESTE   Fie, thou dishonest Satan! Say'st thou the house is dark?

MALVOLIO   As hell, Sir Topaz!

FESTE   Madman, thou errest. There is no darkness but ignorance. Fare thee well.

MALVOLIO   Sir Topaz, Sir Topaz!

SIR TOBY   To him, in thine own voice! (*Sir Toby and Maria depart.*)

FESTE (*in his own voice*) Alas, sir, how fell you beside your five wits?

MALVOLIO I am as well in my wits, fool, as thou art.

FESTE But as well? Then you are mad indeed, if you be no better in your wits than a fool!

MALVOLIO Good fool, help me to some light and some paper. I tell thee I am as well in my wits as any man in Illyria! Some ink, paper and light, and convey what I will set down to my lady!

FESTE (*sings*)

> I am gone, sir, and anon, sir,
> I'll be with you again . . .

In Olivia's garden, Sebastian muses on his good fortune.

SEBASTIAN This may be some error, but no madness, yet doth this accident and flood of fortune so far exceed all instance, all discourse, that I am ready to distrust mine eyes, and wrangle with my reason that persuades me to any other trust but that I am mad, or else the lady's mad . . . But here the lady comes!

Olivia approaches, dragging in her wake, a priest, a real one.

OLIVIA Blame not this haste of mine. If you mean well, now go with me and with this holy man into the chantry by; there before him, plight me the full assurance of your faith. What do you say?

Sebastian stares about him, as if weighing up all the advantages of the match.

SEBASTIAN I'll follow this good man, and go with you, and having sworn truth, ever will be true.

OLIVIA Then lead the way, good father.

Vigorously, she propels the priest towards the chapel wherein all her dreams will soon come true.

Outside the gate of the mansion, the duke and Viola, with lords in attendance, approach. Feste, leaning against the gatepost, bows and holds out his hand. The duke drops a coin into it.

DUKE If you will let your lady know I am here to speak with her and bring her along with you, it may awaken my bounty further.

Feste departs into the house. A group of officers approach. In their midst is their prisoner, Antonio.

104

VIOLA   Here comes the man, sir, that did rescue me.

OFFICER   Orsino, this is that Antonio that took the
            Phoenix –

VIOLA   He did me kindness, sir –

DUKE   Notable pirate, what foolish boldness
            brought thee –

ANTONIO   A witchcraft drew me hither. That most
            ungrateful boy there by your side! For his sake
            did I expose myself into the danger of this
            adverse town; drew to defend him when he was
            beset; where, being apprehended, his false
            cunning denied me mine own purse, which
            I had recommended to his use not half an
            hour before!

VIOLA   How can this be?

            *Olivia, attended, appears at the gate. She
            sees Viola.*

OLIVIA   Cesario, you do not keep promise with me.

VIOLA   Madam –

DUKE   Gracious Olivia –

OLIVIA   (*ignoring the duke*) What do you say, Cesario?

VIOLA   My lord would speak –

OLIVIA   If it be aught to the old tune, my lord, it is
as fat and fulsome to mine ear as howling
after music.

DUKE   Still so cruel?

OLIVIA   Still so constant, my lord.

Orsino sighs, and turns to Viola

DUKE   Come, boy, with me. (*The duke turns to leave.
Viola does likewise.*)

OLIVIA   Where goes Cesario?

VIOLA   After him I love.

OLIVIA   Hast thou forgot thyself? Is it so long?

DUKE   Come away.

OLIVIA   Cesario, husband, stay!

DUKE   Husband?

OLIVIA   Ay, husband. Can he deny?

DUKE   (*to Viola*) Her husband, sirrah?

VIOLA   Not I, my lord!

                As all look to one another in disgust, anger, and
                uncomprehending terror, the priest appears.

OLIVIA   O welcome, father! I charge thee, by thy
                reverence, here to unfold what thou dost know
                hath newly passed between this youth and me.

PRIEST   A contract of eternal bond of love –

DUKE   O thou dissembling cub! Farewell, and
                take her –

VIOLA   (*in tears*) My lord, I do protest –

                Sir Andrew comes staggering, bleeding from
                his head.

SIR ANDREW   (*gasping*) For the love of God, a surgeon! Send
                one presently to Sir Toby!

OLIVIA   Who has done this, Sir Andrew?

SIR ANDREW   The Count's gentleman, one Cesario.
                'Od's lifelings, here he is! You broke my head
                for nothing!

VIOLA   Why do you speak to me? I never hurt you.

*Now comes Sir Toby, also bleeding, and assisted
by Feste.*

DUKE   How now, gentleman, how is't with you?

SIR TOBY   That's all one. H'as hurt me, (*pointing to Viola*)
and there's th'end on't.

OLIVIA   Get him to bed, and let his hurt be looked to.

*Sir Andrew, Sir Toby and Feste depart. No sooner
have they gone than Sebastian appears.*

SEBASTIAN   I am sorry, madam, I have hurt your kinsman:
But had it been the brother of my blood, I must
have done no less with wit and safety. You
throw a strange regard upon me, and by that I
do perceive it hath offended you. Pardon me,
sweet one, even for the vows we made each
other but so late ago.

*All are suddenly dumb with amazement, as they
look from Sebastian to Viola.*

DUKE   One face, one voice, one habit, and two
persons! A natural perspective, that is, and
is not!

SEBASTIAN   (*seeing Antonio*) Antonio, O my dear Antonio!
             How have the hours racked and tortured me,
             since I have lost thee!

ANTONIO   Sebastian are you?

OLIVIA   Most wonderful!

             Sebastian and Viola now see one another.

SEBASTIAN   Do I stand there? I never had a brother. What
             kin are you to me?

VIOLA   Sebastian was my father; such a Sebastian was
             my brother too: so went he suited to his watery
             tomb. If spirits can assume both form and suit,
             you come to fright us.

SEBASTIAN   Thrice welcome, drowned Viola! (*To Olivia*) So
             comes it, lady, you have been mistook. You
             would have been contracted to a maid; nor are
             you therein, by my life, deceived: you are
             betrothed both to a maid and man.

             Olivia stares uncertainly at her husband.

DUKE   Be not amazed, right noble is his blood. (*Olivia
             and Sebastian join hands.*) If this be so, as yet the
             glass seems true, I shall have share in this most

happy wreck. (*To Viola*) Boy, thou hast said to me a thousand times thou never shouldst love woman like me.

VIOLA   And all those sayings will I over-swear!

DUKE   Give me thy hand. You shall from this time be your master's mistress!

OLIVIA   (*gazing from Sebastian to Viola*) A sister! You are she!

In the midst of all the embracings and smiles comes Malvolio, unkempt, with straw in his hair and rage in his eyes. Feste follows.

MALVOLIO   Madam, you have done me wrong, notorious wrong!

OLIVIA   Have I, Malvolio? No.

MALVOLIO   Lady, you have. Pray you, peruse that letter. (*Gives her the fatal letter.*) You must not now deny it is your hand. Tell me, in the modesty of honour, why you have given me such clear lights of favour, bade me come smiling and cross-gartered to you? Why have you suffered me to be imprisoned, kept in a dark house? Tell me, why?

OLIVIA   Alas, Malvolio, this is not my writing –

FESTE   Good madam, hear me speak. Most freely I
                confess, myself and Toby set this device against
                Malvolio here. Maria writ the letter, at Sir
                Toby's great importance, in recompense
                whereof he hath married her –

OLIVIA   Alas, poor fool, how have they baffled thee.

MALVOLIO   I'll be revenged on the whole pack of you!

                He stalks away in high indignation.

OLIVIA   He hath been most notoriously abused.

DUKE   Pursue him, and entreat him to a peace.
                Cesario, come; for so you shall be while you are
                a man; but when in other habits you are seen,
                Orsino's mistress and his fancy's queen.

                *The lovers, in pairs, go within the mansion gates.
                Only Feste is left behind. He seats himself outside
                the gate and sings:*

FESTE   When that I was and a little tiny boy,
                    With hey, ho, the wind and the rain,
                    A foolish thing was but a toy,
                    For the rain it raineth every day.
                    But when I came to man's estate,

With hey, ho, the wind and the rain,
'Gainst knaves and thieves men shut their
                                        gate,
For the rain it raineth every day.
A great while ago the world begun,
With hey, ho, the wind and the rain,
But that's all one, our play is done,
And we'll strive to please you every day.

The curtain falls . . .

Othello

This is the story of a great general, a man in whom the state of Venice has put all its trust, a black man of immense dignity and splendour who is brought to madness, murder and suicide by the skilful lies of the lieutenant he trusts and calls 'honest Iago'. 'Will you, I pray,' asks the tragically bewildered Othello, when Iago's villainy is discovered, 'demand that demi-devil why he hath thus ensnared my soul and body?' 'Demand me nothing;' answers Iago, 'what you know, you know; from this time forth I never will speak word.'

It is a marvellous, terrifying play, in which Shakespeare, at the very height of his powers, has created, in Iago, the most devilish villain in all drama: most devilish because, although he gives reasons for his hatred of Othello, they are too small for the monstrousness of his revenge.

The Characters in the Play

in order of appearance

OTHELLO	*a noble Moor*
DESDEMONA	*daughter to Brabantio and wife to Othello*
IAGO	*Othello's ensign*
BRABANTIO	*a senator of Venice and Desdemona's father*
DUKE OF VENICE	
RODERIGO	*a Venetian gentleman*
CASSIO	*Othello's lieutenant*
EMILIA	*wife to Iago and lady-in-waiting to Desdemona*
MONTANO	*governor of the garrison*
BIANCA	*mistress to Cassio*
LODOVICO	*kinsman of Brabantio*
	Sailors, officers, gentlemen and attendants

The curtain rises on a chapel. Othello the Moor, commander of all the forces of Venice, is to marry Desdemona. But it is a wedding that causes more rage than joy. Not only to Desdemona's father, Brabantio, but to Iago, Othello's ensign.

IAGO

(*watching Desdemona and Othello*) I do hate him as I hate hell's pains. (*They kiss.*) O, you are well-tuned now! But I'll set down the pegs that make this music, as honest as I am.

Iago rushes through the dim and torchlit streets of Venice. He reaches Brabantio's house and bangs on the door.

IAGO

Signior Brabantio, ho! Awake!

BRABANTIO

What is the matter there?

IAGO

Look to your house, your daughter! Even now, very now, an old black ram is tupping your white ewe! Your daughter and the Moor are now making the beast with two backs!

Brabantio searches his house and discovers his daughter gone. With armed servants, he rushes through the streets to Othello's lodging and thunders on the door.

115

BRABANTIO	Who would be a father?
OTHELLO	Keep up your bright swords for the dew will rust them!
BRABANTIO	O thou foul thief! Where hast thou stowed my daughter?
OTHELLO	Where will you that I go and answer to this charge?

In the council chamber, Brabantio throws himself before the duke and accuses Othello who stands by with Iago.

BRABANTIO	Oh, my daughter is abused, stolen from me and corrupted by witchcraft and medicines!
DUKE	(*to Othello*) What can you say to this?
OTHELLO	That I have ta'en away this old man's daughter, it is most true. True I have married her. This only is the witchcraft I have used . . . Her father loved me, oft invited me, still questioned me the story of my life. She loved me for the dangers I had passed, and I loved her, that she did pity them.

116

The duke and his fellow dignitaries listen entranced to Othello's adventures.

DUKE

I think this tale would win my daughter too. Valiant Othello, we must straight employ you against the general enemy. You must hence tonight.

At the crowded quayside, Venetian ships make ready to set sail for Cyprus. Brabantio shouts to Othello who is already aboard.

BRABANTIO

Look to her, Moor, if thou hast eyes to see: she has deceived her father and may thee! (*He points to another ship on which Desdemona stands.*)

OTHELLO

My life upon her faith!

He waves to Desdemona, who waves back, with a strawberry-spotted handkerchief. Iago watches Othello and salutes him. Othello cordially returns the gesture. Roderigo, an elegant young gallant, sidles up beside Iago, gazing in a love-sick way at Desdemona.

IAGO

(*nudging Roderigo suggestively*) I have told thee often, I hate the Moor. If thou canst cuckold him, thou dost thyself a pleasure, and me a sport.

Roderigo smiles hopefully, and slips some money into Iago's ready hand. He departs.

The fleet sets sail but a storm springs up and before long drives the vessels apart. The first ship to reach Cyprus carries Cassio, a young man Othello has promoted over Iago's head to be his lieutenant; then comes a vessel carrying Iago and his wife Emilia, lady-in-waiting to Othello's bride.

CASSIO (*greeting Desdemona as she disembarks*) O behold, the riches of the ship is come ashore! Hail to thee, lady!

He kneels and kisses his fingers in gallant admiration of Desdemona. She extends her hand, which Cassio takes fondly, and rises, kissing her hand as he does so.

IAGO (*aside*) Very good, well kissed, an excellent courtesy. With as little a web as this will I ensnare as great a fly as Cassio.

DESDEMONA What tidings can you tell me of my lord?

CASSIO He is not yet –

He is interrupted by a cry of 'A sail, A sail!' Desdemona looks eagerly to sea. Cassio kisses Emilia.

118

IAGO

Sir, would she give you so much of her lips as of her tongue she oft bestows on me, you'd have enough.

DESDEMONA

Alas, she has no speech!

CASSIO

Lo, where he comes.

Othello appears and greets Desdemona.

OTHELLO

O, my fair warrior!

DESDEMONA

My dear Othello!

They embrace, as Iago looks on. Then all depart, except for Iago and Roderigo. Iago beckons to Roderigo who draws close.

IAGO

Lieutenant Cassio tonight watches on the court of guard. First, I must tell thee this: Desdemona is directly in love with him.

RODERIGO

I cannot believe that in her; she's full of most blest condition!

IAGO

Blest pudding! Didst thou not see her paddle with the palm of his hand?

RODERIGO

Well?

IAGO	Do you find some occasion to anger Cassio. He's rash, and haply may strike at you. So shall you have a shorter journey to your desires . . .

It is night. In a courtyard, Cassio and a group of officers are seated round a table on which there are bottles of wine. Iago enters.

CASSIO	Welcome, Iago; we must to the watch.

IAGO	Not this hour, lieutenant; I have a stoup of wine –

He produces a bottle, and offers it to Cassio.

CASSIO	Not tonight, good Iago; I have very poor and unhappy brains for drinking.

IAGO	But one cup – (*Cassio protests and turns away. The others try to tempt him.*) If I can fasten but one cup upon him, he'll be as full of quarrel and offence as my young mistress' dog. (*Iago sees that Cassio still resists and approaches him, the bottle in hand.*) Some wine, ho! (*He seizes hold of Cassio affectionately. Music strikes up. Iago sings.*)

And let me the cannikin clink, clink.
And let me the cannikin clink;
A soldier's a man,
O, man's life's but a span,
Why then, let a soldier drink!
Why then, let a soldier drink!

Some wine . . . Cassio!

During the song, Iago begins to whirl Cassio round and round, laughingly forcing wine down his throat. The others join in. The dance becomes wild and whirling. At the height of it, Roderigo appears and taunts Cassio. Madly, drunkenly, Cassio draws his sword.

CASSIO   Villain! Villain, knave!

Roderigo flees. Officers try to restrain Cassio, but he is incensed. He fights and wounds Montano. In the midst of the uproar, Othello enters.

OTHELLO   Hold for your lives! What is the matter, masters? Who began this? (*They all fall back, and leave the wretched, drunken Cassio swaying, with his bloody sword in his hand. Othello looks at him sorrowfully.*) Cassio, I love thee, but never more be officer of mine.

All depart. Cassio is left alone, weeping with shame. Iago insinuates himself beside him.

IAGO

What, are you hurt, lieutenant?

CASSIO

Ay, past all surgery. O, I have lost the immortal part of myself. My reputation, Iago, my reputation!

IAGO

As I am an honest man, I thought you had received some bodily wound.

CASSIO

Drunk! And speak like a parrot! O God.

IAGO

Come, come, I'll tell you what you shall do. Our general's wife is now the general. Confess yourself freely to her, importune her – she'll help to put you in your place again.

CASSIO

You advise me well. I will beseech the virtuous Desdemona to undertake for me. Good night, honest Iago.

Iago smiles after him.

IAGO

For whiles this honest fool plies Desdemona to repair his fortunes, and she for him pleads strongly to the Moor, I'll pour this pestilence into his ear: that

122

she repeals him for her body's lust. So will I turn her virtue into pitch, and out of her own goodness make the net that shall enmesh them all!

Next morning, Cassio takes Iago's advice. He approaches Desdemona in the palace garden and begs her to plead his cause with Othello.

DESDEMONA   Be thou assured, good Cassio, I will do all my abilities in thy behalf. (*Cassio, ever the gentleman, fervently kisses her hand. She laughs.*) Therefore be merry, Cassio –

EMILIA   Madam, here comes my lord!

CASSIO   (*hastily*) Madam, I'll take my leave.

He hastens away as Othello appears, accompanied by Iago. Iago glares at the retreating Cassio.

IAGO   Ha! I like not that.

OTHELLO   What dost thou say?

IAGO   Nothing my lord.

OTHELLO   Was not that Cassio that parted from my wife?

IAGO   Cassio, my lord? No, sure I cannot think it, that he would steal away so guilty-like, seeing you coming.

OTHELLO   I do believe 'twas he. Is he not honest?

IAGO   My lord, for aught I know.

Othello stares at Iago, who shakes his head, looking at Desdemona.

OTHELLO   I think so too.

IAGO   Why, then I think Cassio's an honest man.

OTHELLO   I know thou art full of honesty, and weigh'st thy words. Thou dost mean something . . .

IAGO   Oh, beware jealousy, my lord! It is the green-eyed monster.

OTHELLO   Farewell, if more thou dost perceive, let me know more. (*Iago leaves. Othello gazes towards Desdemona.*) Excellent wretch! Perdition catch my soul but I do love thee; and when I love thee not, chaos is come again!

DESDEMONA Good love, call him back.

OTHELLO   Who is't you mean?

DESDEMONA   Why, your lieutenant, Cassio.

OTHELLO   Not now, sweet Desdemona, some
                 other time.

DESDEMONA   Shall't be tonight at supper?

OTHELLO   No, not tonight.

DESDEMONA   Why then, tomorrow night –

OTHELLO   I do beseech thee, to leave me but a little
                 by myself.

DESDEMONA   Are you not well?

OTHELLO   I have a pain upon my forehead here.

DESDEMONA   Let me but bind your head, within this
                 hour it will be well again.

OTHELLO   Your napkin is too little. (*He pushes the
                 handkerchief aside and she drops it.*)
                 Let it alone.

                 Emilia, left behind, picks up the handkerchief.

EMILIA   This was her first remembrance from the

Moor. My wayward husband hath a hundred times wooed me to steal it; but she so loves the token –

Iago enters.

IAGO

What do you here alone?

EMILIA

I have a thing for you. What will you give me now for that same handkerchief?

IAGO

A good wench! Give it to me. (*He snatches it.*) I will in Cassio's lodging lose this napkin and let him find it. Trifles light as air are to the jealous confirmations strong as proofs of holy writ. This may do something. The Moor already changes with my poison . . .

As he speaks, Othello approaches. His countenance is tormented as his fearful thoughts present him, over and over again, with the vision of Cassio kissing his wife's hand, until the kiss becomes lascivious.

IAGO

Look where he comes! Not poppy nor mandragora, nor all the drowsy syrups of the world, shall ever medicine thee to that sweet sleep which thou owed'st yesterday.

OTHELLO	(*seizing Iago by the throat*) Villain, be sure thou prove my love a whore! Or woe upon thy life!
IAGO	(*freeing himself*) O grace! O heaven defend me! Take note, take note, O world! To be direct and honest is not safe.

He retreats.

OTHELLO	Nay, stay; give me a living reason, that she's disloyal.
IAGO	I do not like the office; but I will go on. I lay with Cassio lately. In sleep, I heard him say, 'Sweet Desdemona, let us be wary, let us hide our loves'.
OTHELLO	O monstrous, monstrous!
IAGO	Nay, this was but his dream –
OTHELLO	I'll tear her all to pieces!
IAGO	Nay, yet be wise; she may be honest yet. Have you not seen a handkerchief spotted with strawberries in your wife's hand?
OTHELLO	I gave her such a one; 'twas my first gift.

IAGO

I know not that; but such a handkerchief
– I am sure it was your wife's – did I today
see Cassio wipe his beard with.

OTHELLO

O blood, Iago, blood! Within these three days
let me hear thee say that Cassio's not alive.

IAGO

My friend is dead: 'tis done as you request.
But let her live.

OTHELLO

Damn her, lewd minx! Come, go with me
apart. Now art thou my lieutenant.

IAGO

I am your own for ever.

*In another part of the garden, Desdemona
searches for the lost handkerchief. Emilia is
with her.*

DESDEMONA

Where should I lose that handkerchief,
Emilia?

EMILIA

I know not, madam.

Othello enters.

DESDEMONA

How is't with you, my lord?

OTHELLO

I have a salt and sorry rheum offends me;
lend me thy handkerchief.

DESDEMONA	Here, my lord.
OTHELLO	That which I gave you.
DESDEMONA	I have it not about me.
OTHELLO	That's a fault. That handkerchief did an Egyptian to my mother give. She told her, while she kept it, 'twould subdue my father entirely to her love; but if she lost it or made a gift of it, my father's eye should hold her loathly . . .
DESDEMONA	Then would to God that I had never seen't!
OTHELLO	Is't lost? Is't gone?
DESDEMONA	Heaven bless us! This is a trick to put me from my suit. Pray you let Cassio be received again.
OTHELLO	Fetch me that handkerchief.
DESDEMONA	I pray, talk me of Cassio.
OTHELLO	The handkerchief!

He rushes away like a madman. But the handkerchief has gone. Iago has put it in

Cassio's lodging and Cassio, finding it and liking it, has given it to Bianca, his mistress, to copy.

Still searching for the handkerchief, Desdemona and Emilia leave the garden and presently Iago and Othello enter together. Othello leans almost pathetically, towards his new lieutenant. He is sweating and seems unwell.

OTHELLO What hath he said?

IAGO Faith, that he did – I know not what he did.

OTHELLO But, what?

IAGO Lie –

OTHELLO With her?

IAGO With her, on her, what you will.

OTHELLO Lie with her? Lie on her? Handkerchief – confessions – handkerchief! Is't possible? O devil!

During the above wild outburst. Othello is overwhelmed by hateful fancies, which finally dissolve into a red oblivion, like the fires of hell. Gradually the fragmented images solidify into Iago's face, looking down, much concerned.

IAGO

How is it, general? Whilst you were here, mad with your grief, Cassio came hither. I shifted him away; bade him anon return and here speak with me. Do but encave yourself, for I will make him tell the tale anew, where, how, how oft, how long ago, and when he has and is again to cope your wife. Will you withdraw?

Othello, helplessly in the power of Iago, nods and hides himself behind a trellis, like a netted beast. Cassio approaches.

IAGO

(*to himself*) Now will I question Cassio of Bianca. As he shall smile, Othello shall go mad.

Iago, with the skill of a dancer, leads Cassio, whispering in his ear, close to the trellis behind which Othello listens.

IAGO

(*to Cassio, aloud*) I never knew a woman love man so.

CASSIO   (*laughing*) Alas, poor rogue! I think i' faith she loves me. She hangs and lolls and weeps upon me, so hales and pulls me . . .

OTHELLO   Now he tells how she plucked him to my chamber. O, I see that nose of yours, but not the dog I shall throw it to!

Bianca enters. She is clutching the handkerchief.

BIANCA   (*flourishing it*) This is some minx's token, and I must take out the work? There!

OTHELLO   By heaven, that should be my handkerchief!

Bianca throws the handkerchief at Cassio, and stalks away indignantly.

IAGO   After her, after her!

CASSIO   Faith, I must. She'll rail in the streets else. (*He follows.*)

OTHELLO   (*emerging from concealment*) How shall I murder him, Iago? I would have him nine years a-killing. A fine woman, a fair woman, a sweet woman!

IAGO   Nay, you must forget that.

OTHELLO   No, my heart is turned to stone. I strike it, and it hurts my hand. O, the world hath not a sweeter creature! O Iago, the pity of it, Iago!

IAGO   If you are so fond over her iniquity –

OTHELLO   Get me some poison, Iago, this night. This night, Iago!

IAGO   Do it not with poison; strangle her in her bed, even the bed she hath contaminated. And for Cassio, let me be his undertaker.

OTHELLO   Good, good! The justice of it pleases.

A trumpet sounds. The two men stare. At the harbour, Lodovico, the ambassador from the duke, disembarks and is greeted by Desdemona. Othello, accompanied by Iago, appears and Lodovico gives him a letter.

LODOVICO   (*to Othello*) The Duke and Senators of Venice greet you. (*To Desdemona*) How does Lieutenant Cassio?

Frowning, Othello moves away, reading.

DESDEMONA	Cousin, there's fallen between him and my lord an unkind breach; I would do much to atone them, for the love I bear to Cassio.
OTHELLO	Devil! (*He strikes her.*)
DESDEMONA	(*weeping*) I have not deserved this.
LODOVICO	(*comforting her*) Maybe the letter moved him for as I think they do command him home. (*To Othello*) My lord, make her amends; she weeps.
OTHELLO	O devil, devil! Out of my sight! (*Bewildered, Desdemona departs.*) Sir, I obey the mandate, and will return to Venice.

Othello rushes away.

LODOVICO	(*to Iago*) Is this the noble Moor whom our full senate call all-in-all sufficient? Are his wits safe?
IAGO	Alas, alas! It is not honesty in me to speak what I have seen and known. Do but go after and mark how he continues . . .

Desdemona's bedchamber. She is seated with Emilia. Othello enters.

OTHELLO	Let me see your eyes; look in my face. (*He dismisses Emilia with a wave of his hand. She goes.*) What art thou?
DESDEMONA	Your wife, my lord, your true and loyal wife.
OTHELLO	Are you not a strumpet?
DESDEMONA	No, as I shall be saved!
OTHELLO	I cry you mercy. I took you for that cunning whore of Venice that married with Othello.
	He rushes from the room. Emilia returns with Iago, to comfort Desdemona.
EMILA	How do you, madam?
IAGO	What is the matter, my lady?
EMILIA	He called her whore.
DESDEMONA	O good Iago, what shall I do to win my lord again?
IAGO	'Tis but his humour, the business of the state does him offence, and he does chide with you. Weep not, all things shall be well. (*He leaves.*)

DESDEMONA   (*as Emilia unpins her hair and begins to brush it.*) How foolish are our minds! My mother had a maid called Barbary, and he she loved proved mad, and did forsake her; she had a song of 'willow', and she died singing it; that song tonight will not go from my mind.

EMILIA   Come, come, you talk.

DESDEMONA   (*singing*)
The poor soul sat sighing by a
                    sycamore tree,
Sing all a green willow;
Her hand on her bosom, her head on
                    her knee,
Sing willow, willow, willow,
Sing willow, willow, willow,
Must be my garland . . .

As she sings, Othello, by an open window, hears the song faintly. He frowns and stares down into the dark town below. There, Iago waits in the street near the palace for Roderigo.

IAGO   If thou hast purpose, courage, valour, then this night show it.

RODERIGO   I have no great devotion to the deed . . .

136

IAGO   Fear nothing, I'll be at thy elbow.

Cassio bids farewell to Bianca and comes out into the street.

IAGO   (*to himself*) Whether he kill Cassio, or Cassio him, or each do kill the other, every way makes my game.

A scuffle of shadows. Roderigo attacks Cassio. He falls and is himself wounded. He crawls away. Iago darts forward and stabs Cassio from behind, and then vanishes into concealment. There are shouts and cries.

CASSIO   Help, ho! Murder, murder!

Othello, still by the window, hears the shout.

OTHELLO   The voice of Cassio: Iago keeps his word. O brave Iago, thou hast such noble sense of thy friend's wrong! Thou teachest me . . . (*He leaves the room.*)

The street is alive with torches and anxious faces, surrounding the wounded Cassio. Among them are Lodovico and Iago.

IAGO   O my lieutenant! What villains have done this?

A voice calls from the shadows.

RODERIGO'S VOICE   O, help me here!

CASSIO   That's one of them!

IAGO   (*finding Roderigo*) O murderous slave! (*He stabs him.*)

RODERIGO   O damned Iago! O inhuman dog! (*He dies.*)

IAGO   (*staring up towards the castle from which Othello has looked down*) This is the night that either makes me, or fordoes me quite.

In her bedchamber, Desdemona lies on her bed. She closes her eyes. Quietly, Othello enters. He gazes first at the sleeping Desdemona, then at the candle beside her.

OTHELLO   Put out the light, and then put out the light: if I quench thee, thou flaming minister, I can again thy former light restore, should I repent me; but once put out thy light – (*He frowns, then bends to kiss her.*)

DESDEMONA   Othello?

OTHELLO	Ay, Desdemona.
DESDEMONA	Will you come to bed, my lord?
OTHELLO	Have you prayed tonight, Desdemona?
DESDEMONA	Ay, my lord.
OTHELLO	If you bethink yourself of any crime unreconciled as yet to heaven and grace, solicit for it straight. I would not kill thy unprepared spirit.
DESDEMONA	Then heaven have mercy on me!
OTHELLO	The handkerchief which I so loved, and gave thee, thou gavest to Cassio.
DESDEMONA	I never gave it him, send for him hither –
OTHELLO	He has confessed.
DESDEMONA	What, my lord?
OTHELLO	That he hath . . . used thee.
DESDEMONA	He will not say so!
OTHELLO	No, his mouth is stopped.

DESDEMONA   Alas, he is betrayed, and I undone!

                   Othello seizes a pillow.

OTHELLO   Down, strumpet!

DESDEMONA   Kill me tomorrow, let me live tonight!

OTHELLO   Nay, an' you strive –

DESDEMONA   But half an hour!

OTHELLO   It is too late!

                   *He presses the pillow down on her face to
                   suffocate her. There is a knocking on
                   the door.*

EMILIA'S VOICE   My lord, my lord!

OTHELLO   'Tis Emilia! If she come in, she'll sure
                   speak to my wife – my wife, my wife!
                   What wife? I have no wife! O
                   insupportable –

EMILIA   I do beseech you that I may speak
                   with you!

OTHELLO   O, come in, Emilia.

He draws the bed curtains and goes to unlock the door. Emilia enters and moves towards the bed.

DESDEMONA   (*faintly*) O falsely, falsely murdered!

EMILIA   (*rushing to draw back the bed curtains*) O, lady, speak again! Who hath done this deed?

DESDEMONA   Nobody; I myself. Commend me to my kind lord. O farewell. (*She dies.*)

OTHELLO   She's like a liar gone to burning hell: 'twas I that killed her!

EMILIA   O, the more angel she, and you the blacker devil!

OTHELLO   She was as false as water!

EMILIA   Thou as rash as fire to say that she was false!

OTHELLO   Cassio did top her: ask thy husband else.

EMILIA   My husband?

OTHELLO   Ay, 'twas he that told me first –

EMILIA	My husband?
OTHELLO	I say thy husband. My friend, thy husband, honest, honest Iago.
EMILIA	If he say so, may his pernicious soul rot half a grain a day! Help, help, ho! help! The Moor hath killed my mistress!

Montano and Iago burst into the room. They see the murdered Desdemona.

MONTANO	O monstrous act!
OTHELLO	'Tis pitiful; but yet Iago knows that she with Cassio hath the act of shame a thousand times committed. Cassio confessed it, and she did gratify his amorous works with the recognisance and pledge of love which I first gave her. I saw it in his hand: it was a handkerchief.
EMILIA	'Twill out, it will out! O thou dull Moor, that handkerchief thou speakest on I found by fortune and did give my husband. He begged of me to steal it –

IAGO	Filth, thou liest!

He stabs Emilia from behind, and escapes. Emilia falls, dying, on the bed. Montano pursues Iago.

EMILIA	(*dying*) Moor, she was chaste; she loved thee, cruel Moor.

She dies. Othello gazes down upon the dead Desdemona. With horror he begins to understand the full extent of Iago's treachery.

OTHELLO	O ill-starred wench! Pale as thy smock! When we shall meet at compt this look of thine will hurl my soul from heaven and fiends will snatch at it. Cold, cold my girl, even like thy chastity.

Montano, Lodovico, and the wounded Cassio enter with Iago, guarded. Othello stares at Iago, and approaches him.

OTHELLO	If that thou be'st a devil, I cannot kill thee. (*He wounds him with his sword. At once, soldiers disarm him.*)
IAGO	I bleed, sir, but not killed.

LODOVICO	This wretch hath part confessed his villainy.
CASSIO	Dear general, I did never give you cause.
OTHELLO	I do believe it, and I ask your pardon. Will you, I pray, demand that demi-devil why he hath thus ensnared my soul and body?
IAGO	Demand me nothing; what you know, you know. From this time forth I never will speak word.
LODOVICO	(to Othello) You must forsake this room and go with us –
OTHELLO	Soft you, a word or two. I have done the state some service and they know't. I pray you in your letters when you shall these unlucky deeds relate, speak of them as they are; nothing extenuate nor set down aught in malice. Then must you speak of one that loved not wisely, but too well. Set you down this and say besides that in Aleppo once where a malignant and a turbaned Turk beat a Venetian and traduced the state, I took by the throat the circumcised dog and smote him thus! (He stabs himself and falls beside

144

Desdemona.) I kissed thee ere I killed thee:
no way but this, killing myself, to die
upon a kiss.

The curtain falls.

The Taming of the Shrew

Written, probably, in 1592, when the playwright was twenty-eight, *The Taming of the Shrew* is one of Shakespeare's earliest comedies. It is also one of his funniest. For four hundred years, the antics of Kate and Petruchio, as they trade insults, blows and kisses on their stormy way from courtship to marriage to perfect love and understanding, have filled the world's theatres with laughter and delight. But there is more to the play than a knockabout, boisterous battle of the sexes. It is a play about change, about transformation, about the magic of the theatre itself, when, at one moment, we are watching a group of people in strange costume strutting about on bare boards, and the next, we are in a street in sunny Padua, watching old Baptista Minola, trying to marry off his turbulent daughter Kate to whoever is brave enough to take her . . .

146

The Characters in the Play

in order of appearance

CHRISTOPHER SLY	*a tinker*
THE HOSTESS OF THE INN	
A LORD	
TWO SERVANTS	
BAPTISTA	*a rich citizen of Padua*
KATERINA	*his elder daughter*
BIANCA	*his younger daughter*
GREMIO	*a rich old citizen of Padua, suitor to Bianca*
HORTENSIO	*a gentleman of Padua, suitor to Bianca*
PETRUCHIO	*a gentleman of Verona, suitor to Katerina*
SERVANT	
GRUMIO	*servant to Petruchio*
LUCENTIO	*a gentleman of Pisa, suitor to Bianca*
NATHANIEL	*a servant*
PETER	*a servant*
TAILOR	
A RICH WIDOW	

147

The curtain rises on the outside of a country inn. Christopher Sly, the tinker, is drunk. Indeed, he is not often sober; and the hostess of the inn where he does his drinking has had enough of him.

HOSTESS'S VOICE   A pair of stocks, you rogue!

> *The door bursts open and out staggers Sly. He slides down the tethering post, and finishes up on the ground. He sleeps, his mouth wide open – a picture of drunken brutishness. There is a winding of horns. Enter a lord from hunting, with his train. He sees the recumbent Sly.*

LORD   Grim death, how foul and loathsome is thy visage. (*Sly stirs, hiccups and snores.*)

SLY   The Slys are no rogues.

> *The lord starts back. He frowns, then smiles, as a thought strikes him. He beckons his servants about him.*

LORD   (*confidentially*) Sirs, I will practise on this drunken man.

> *The drunken Sly is transported to the lord's mansion where he is wrapped in new clothes, rings put upon his fingers, a banquet laid for him, and servants ordered to wait upon him as if he was indeed the lord of the mansion.*

148

SLY   (*waking*) For God's sake, a pot of small ale!

1ST SERVANT   Your honour –

2ND SERVANT   Your lordship –

SLY   Call me not 'honour', nor 'lordship'. Am I
               not Christopher Sly, old Sly's son of
               Burton Heath?

LORD   Thou art a lord and nothing but a lord.

2ND SERVANT   These fifteen years you have been in
               a dream.

SLY   These fifteen years! By my fay, a goodly
               nap! Upon my life, I am a lord indeed!

1ST SERVANT   Your doctors thought it good you hear
               a play and frame your mind to mirth
               and merriment.

SLY   Well, we'll see it.

               *Sly is led from his bed to a great hall, at the
               farthest end of which is a curtained stage. The
               performance is about to begin.*

               *The curtain rises on a street in Padua. Enter
               Baptista with his two daughters, Katerina and*

Bianca, together with Bianca's suitors, young Hortensio and old Gremio.

BAPTISTA Gentlemen, importune me no farther for how I firmly am resolved you know – that is, not to bestow my youngest daughter before I have a husband for the elder. If either of you both love Katerina, leave shall you have to court her at your pleasure.

While her father speaks, Katerina – Kate – a wild and fearsome lass, is doing her best, by means of surreptitious pinches, kicks and tweakings of her fair plaits, to make her angel sister Bianca's life a misery.

GREMIO To cart her rather! She's too rough for me!

KATE (*to Baptista*) I pray you, sir, is it your will to make a stale of me amongst these mates?

HORTENSIO 'Mates', maid? No mates for you unless you were of gentler, milder mould. (*Kate threatens him with her fist. Hortensio backs away.*) From all such devils, good Lord deliver us!

GREMIO (*skipping behind Hortensio*) And me too, good Lord!

BAPTISTA   Bianca, get you in. (*She looks downcast.*) And
             let it not displease thee, good Bianca, for I
             will love thee ne'er the less, my girl.

KATE   (*pulling Bianca's hair*) A pretty peat!

BIANCA   Sister, content you in my discontent. Sir,
             to your pleasure I humbly subscribe. (*She
             goes towards the door of her house, picking up
             a pretty guitar hung with ribbons and trailing
             it behind her.*)

GREMIO   Why, will you mew her up, Signor
             Baptista, for this fiend of hell?

             *As she dawdles, we see Lucentio, a young
             gallant, peering round a pillar at Bianca –
             obviously much attracted!*

BAPTISTA   Gentlemen, content ye. I am resolved.
             (*Bianca goes into the house. Baptista follows,
             then pauses and turns to Kate.*) Katerina,
             you may stay. (*He goes in.*)

KATE   Why, and I trust I may go too, may I
             not? Ha!

             *She flounces into the house and slams the door
             violently. The gentlemen look at one another.
             Comes another loud bang as another door is*

151

slammed. They jump, and Lucentio does too.

It was a wretched state of affairs! No matter the suitors' sighs, old Baptista would never give his consent to the marriage of the fair Bianca until a husband was found for Katerina. And no consent, no dowry.

The scene changes to Petruchio, a gentleman from Verona, on horseback, knocking at Hortensio's window. Hortensio greets him enthusiastically.

HORTENSIO

My good friend Petruchio! What happy gale blows you to Padua here from old Verona?

PETRUCHIO

Such wind as scatters young men through the world. Signor Hortensio, I come to wive it weathily in Padua; if wealthily, then happily in Padua.

HORTENSIO

(*thoughtfully*) I can, Petruchio, help thee to a wife with wealth enough, and young, and beauteous, brought up as best becomes a gentlewoman. Her only fault – and that is faults enough – is that she is intolerable curst, and shrewd and froward. I would not wed her for a mine of gold!

PETRUCHIO   Hortensio, peace. Thou know'st not gold's
              effect. I will not sleep, Hortensio, till I
              see her . . .

              Outside Baptista's house. Kate emerges,
              followed by a weeping Bianca, her hands tied.

BIANCA   Good sister, wrong me not, nor wrong
              yourself, to make a bondmaid and a slave
              of me.

              Kate, detecting spite in the last remark, drags
              Bianca to the fountain, Baptista appears.

BAPTISTA   Why, how now dame, whence grows this
              insolence? Poor girl, she weeps. (*He unties*
              her hands and turns to Kate.) For shame,
              thou hilding of a devilish spirit, why dost
              thou wrong her that did ne'er wrong thee?
              Bianca, get thee in.

              Bianca goes in.

KATE   Nay, now I see she is your treasure, she
              must have a husband, I must dance
              barefoot on her wedding day! Talk not to
              me, I will go sit and weep, till I can find
              occasion for revenge! (*She rushes into*
              the house, with the inevitable slamming of
              the door.)

153

BAPTISTA Was ever gentleman thus grieved as I? But who comes here?

Enter Petruchio, who greets Baptista courteously.

PETRUCHIO I am a gentleman of Verona, sir. Petruchio is my name. Pray have you not a daughter called Katerina, fair and virtuous?

BAPTISTA I have a daughter, sir, called Katerina.

PETRUCHIO Signor Baptista, my business asketh haste, and every day I cannot come to woo. Then tell me, if I get your daughter's love, what dowry shall I have with her to wife?

BAPTISTA (*looking startled*) After my death the one half of my lands, and in possession twenty thousand crowns.

PETRUCHIO (*nodding approvingly*) Let covenants be therefore drawn between us.

BAPTISTA (*suddenly overcome with conscience*) Ay, where the special thing is well obtained, that is, her love; for that is all in all.

PETRUCHIO Why, that is nothing; for I tell you, father, I am as peremptory as she proud-minded,

and when two raging fires meet together
they do consume the thing that feeds
their fury.

BAPTISTA

Well mayst thou woo, and happy be thy
speed! Be thou armed for some unhappy
words. Shall I send my daughter Kate
to you?

PETRUCHIO

I pray you do, I'll attend her here . . .
(*Baptista, unable to believe his good fortune,
hastens within. Petruchio is alone.*)

*Kate appears. She eyes Petruchio curiously, as
he does her. It is plain that an instant interest
has been kindled between them, and they
regard one another as worthy adversaries.*

PETRUCHIO

Good morrow, Kate – for that's your
name, I hear.

KATE

Well have you heard, but something hard
of hearing; they call me Katherine that do
talk of me.

PETRUCHIO

You lie, in faith, for you are called plain
Kate, and bonny Kate, and sometimes
Kate the curst. But Kate, the prettiest
Kate in Christendom, hearing thy
mildness praised in every town, thy virtues

spoke of, and thy beauty sounded, myself
am moved to woo thee for a wife!

KATE   'Moved', in good time! Let him that
          moved you hither remove you hence!

PETRUCHIO Come, come, you wasp, i' faith, you are
          too angry.

KATE   If I be waspish, best beware my sting!

PETRUCHIO My remedy then is to pluck it out!

KATE   Ay, if the fool could find it where it lies.

PETRUCHIO Who knows not where a wasp does wear
          his sting? In his tail. (*He puts his hand on
          her bottom. She breaks loose.*)

KATE   And so farewell! (*She turns to go.*)

PETRUCHIO Nay, come again. Good Kate, I am
          a gentleman –

KATE   That I'll try! (*She strikes him.*)

PETRUCHIO I swear I'll cuff you if you strike again!

KATE   If you strike me you are no gentleman.
          (*They struggle.*)

PETRUCHIO   In sooth, you scape not so!

KATE   Let me go!

PETRUCHIO   (*releasing her so suddenly that she falls*) Why does the world report that Kate doth limp? O sland'rous world! Kate like the hazel twig is straight and slender. O let me see thee walk. Thou dost not halt.

KATE   Go, fool.

PETRUCHIO   Am I not wise?

KATE   Yes, keep you warm.

PETRUCHIO   Marry, so I mean, sweet Katherine, in thy bed. Now, Kate, I am a husband for your turn. For I am he am born to tame you, Kate, and bring you from a wild Kate to a Kate conformable as other household Kates.

It is apparent that Kate, in spite of herself, is much attracted to Petruchio, and his praise of her beauty does not go unnoticed. Old Baptista arrives.

BAPTISTA   Now, Signor Petruchio, how speed you with my daughter?

PETRUCHIO   How but well, sir? We have 'greed so
                well together that upon Sunday is the
                wedding day!

KATE   I'll see thee hanged on Sunday first.

                *Petruchio laughs, and confides to Baptista,
                unheard by Kate.*

PETRUCHIO   'Tis bargained 'twixt us twain, being
                alone, that she shall still be curst in
                company. I tell you 'tis incredible to
                believe how much she loves me! O, the
                kindest Kate! She hung about my neck,
                and kiss on kiss she vied so fast, that in a
                twink she won me to her love!

BAPTISTA   I know not what to say, but give me your
                hands. God send you joy; Petruchio, 'tis
                a match.

PETRUCHIO   Provide the feast, father, and bid the
                guests: I will to Venice; Sunday comes
                apace. We will have rings, and things, and
                fine array. And kiss me, Kate, we will be
                married o' Sunday!

                *Kate glares at Petruchio, then at her father,
                then at Petruchio again. She kisses him; then,
                wiping the kiss off her lips, rushes into the*

house, slamming the door behind her. Baptista looks dismayed; but Petruchio wags a finger as if to say, 'I told you so', and departs. Baptista sighs with relief.

Invitations are dispatched and Kate's wedding-gown is prepared. By Sunday, the bride is ready, and everyone awaits the coming of the bridegroom. They wait, and they wait, and they wait.

KATE I told you, I, he was a frantic fool. Now must the world point at poor Katherine and say, 'Lo, there is mad Petruchio's wife, if it would please him come and marry her!' (*She rushes out weeping in fury and a sense of betrayal.*)

BAPTISTA Go, girl, I cannot blame thee now to weep, for such an injury would vex a saint.

A servant enters, breathless.

SERVANT Master, master, news, and such news as you never heard of!

BAPTISTA Is he come?

For answer, the servant points, and Petruchio, accompanied by his servant, appears. He is

159

dressed in 'a new hat and an old jerkin; a pair of old breeches thrice turned; a pair of boots that have been candle-cases, one buckled, another laced; an old rusty sword . . .' In short, a very scarecrow. He dismounts. The guests watch, amazed.

PETRUCHIO   (*ignoring the stares*) Where is Kate? The morning wears, 'tis time we were in church.

BAPTISTA   But thus I trust you will not marry her.

PETRUCHIO   Good sooth, even thus. To me she's married, not unto my clothes. But what a fool am I to chat with you, when I should bid good morrow to my bride, and seal the title with a lovely kiss! (*He departs.*)

All stare at one another appalled.

In Baptista's house, the wedding guests await the arrival of the happy couple. Petruchio enters with his tousled bride.

PETRUCHIO   Gentlemen and friends, I thank you for your pains. I know you think to dine with me today, but so it is, my haste doth call me hence.

BAPTISTA   Is't possible you will away tonight?

160

PETRUCHIO   I must away before night come.

GREMIO   Let me entreat you to stay 'til after dinner.

PETRUCHIO   It cannot be.

KATE   Let me entreat you. Now if you love
                 me, stay.

PETRUCHIO   Grumio, my horse!

KATE   Nay then, do what thou canst, I will not go
                 today, no, nor tomorrow, not till I please
                 myself. Gentlemen, forward to the bridal
                 dinner. I see a woman may be made a fool
                 if she had not a spirit to resist.

PETRUCHIO   They shall go forward, Kate, at thy
                 command. – Obey the bride, you that
                 attend on her. Go to the feast, and carouse
                 full measure to her maidenhead. But for
                 my bonny Kate, she must with me. I will
                 be master of what is mine own.

                 *Kate shows every sign of defiance and seeks
                 support from her father and the guests. It is
                 not forthcoming. At length, Petruchio seizes
                 her about the waist, and, with fiercely drawn
                 sword, rushes away with her, followed by his
                 servant, Grumio. The guests crowd after them.*

Outside, Kate, Petruchio and Grumio gallop away on three horses. Inside, all is cheerfulness. Bianca is queening it among her admirers.

LUCENTIO   Mistress, what is your opinion of your sister?

BIANCA   That being mad herself, she's madly mated!

The three riders in a wet and windy landscape. Kate's horse stumbles and she tumbles down. The horse bolts. Petruchio hoists Kate up onto his own horse, and away they ride, he behind, she in front, muddy and furious.

At last, they arrive at Petruchio's house in Verona where the servants are making ready for the arrival of the master and his bride.

PETRUCHIO   Where be these knaves? What, no man at door to hold my stirrup nor to take my horse?

ALL SERVANTS   Here sir, here sir, here sir!

PETRUCHIO   Go, rascals, go and fetch my supper in! (*He sings.*) 'Where is the life that late I led?' Be merry, Kate! Some water here!

162

What ho! (*Water is brought.*) Come, Kate, and wash and welcome heartily! (*He stretches out his foot and trips the servant.*) You whoreson villain, will you let it fall? (*He threatens the man.*)

KATE
Patience, I pray you, 'twas a fault unwilling.

Food is set out on a table.

PETRUCHIO
A whoreson, beetle-headed, flap-eared knave! Come, Kate, sit down, I know you have a stomach. (*Kate sits.*) What's this? Mutton?

SERVANT
Ay.

PETRUCHIO
'Tis burnt, and so is all the meat! How durst you villains serve it thus to me?

Petruchio hurls the dishes at the servants, who scatter in terror.

KATE
I pray you, husband, be not so disquiet. The meat was well –

PETRUCHIO
I tell thee, Kate, 'twas burnt and dried away, and I am expressly forbid to touch it, for it engenders choler, planteth anger –

and better 'twere that both of us did fast! Come, I will bring thee to thy bridal chamber.

He pulls the hungry Kate away from the table, and away to their bedroom. The servants begin to clear away the wreckage of the meal.

NATHANIEL   Peter, didst ever see the like?

PETER   He kills her in her own humour.

The servants depart. A moment later, Petruchio appears, very furtively. He peers about him, then, hastily, retrieves whatever food is left, and gobbles it down hungrily. As he munches and swallows, he confides:

PETRUCHIO   Thus have I politicly begun my reign. Last night she slept not, nor tonight she shall not. He that knows better how to tame a shrew, now let him speak . . .

While Kate is learning one lesson, her sister, the fair Bianca, is learning another . . .

In Baptista's house, Bianca is closeted with her new suitor, Lucentio, a rich young man from Pisa, who cunningly disguised as a

schoolmaster has outbid his rivals and won
Bianca's heart.

BIANCA   What, master, read you?

LUCENTIO   The Art to Love.

BIANCA   And may you prove, sir, master of your art!

LUCENTIO   While you, sweet dear, prove mistress of
                my heart.

                He removes his whiskers and kisses her.
                Meanwhile, Hortensio and Gremio give up
                their hopes for Bianca's love: Gremio retires to
                his moneybags, and Hortensio decides to
                marry a rich widow. But first he calls at his
                friend Petruchio's house.

                He finds Kate seated at a table. Petruchio and
                Hortensio enter with a dish of meat.

HORTENSIO   Mistress, what cheer?

KATE   Faith, as cold as can be.

PETRUCHIO   Pluck up thy spirits! Here, love, thou seest
                how diligent I am to dress thy meat
                myself. What, not a word? Nay then, thou
                lov'st it not. Here, take away this dish.

165

A servant comes forward.

KATE   I pray you let it stand.

PETRUCHIO   The poorest service is repaid with thanks,
                  and so shall mine before you touch
                  the meat.

KATE   I thank you, sir.

PETRUCHIO   Kate, eat apace. And now, my honey love,
                  we will return unto thy father's house,
                  and revel it as bravely as the best, with
                  silken coats and caps, and golden rings –
                  what, hast thou dined? (*He takes away
                  her unfinished plate.*) The tailor stays
                  thy leisure.

                  The tailor enters.

TAILOR   Here is the cap your worship did bespeak.

PETRUCHIO   Why, 'tis a cockle or a walnut shell. A
                  baby's cap. Come, let me have a bigger.

KATE   I'll have no bigger. Gentlewomen wear
                  such caps as these.

PETRUCHIO   When you are gentle, you shall have one
                  too, and not till then.

HORTENSIO   That will not be in haste!

PETRUCHIO   Thy gown? Come, tailor, let us see it. (*The
                tailor displays the gown.*) What's this? A
                sleeve? Carved like an apple tart? Here's
                snip and nip, and cut and slish and slash!
                (*The tailor retreats, baffled.*)

HORTENSIO   (*aside*) I see she's like to have neither cap
                nor gown.

PETRUCHIO   I'll none of it! (*To the tailor*) Away, thou
                rag, thou quantity, thou remnant! (*He rips
                the dress. Kate is in despair.*)

KATE   I never saw a better-fashioned gown.

                *Petruchio mutters to Hortensio as
                tailor retreats.*

PETRUCHIO   Hortensio, say thou wilt see the tailor
                paid. Well, come my Kate, we will unto
                your father's, even in these honest mean
                habiliments. Our purses shall be proud,
                our garments poor, for 'tis the mind that
                makes the body rich. Let's see, I think 'tis
                now some seven o'clock, and well we may
                come there by dinner-time.

KATE   I dare assure you, sir, 'tis almost two.

PETRUCHIO   It shall be what o'clock I say it is.

HORTENSIO   (*aside*) Why, so this gallant will command the sun!

              The scene changes to Petruchio, Kate and Hortensio on horseback.

PETRUCHIO   Come on, a God's name, once more towards our father's. Good Lord, how bright and goodly shines the moon!

KATE   The moon? The sun! It is not moonlight now.

PETRUCHIO   I say it is the moon that shines so bright.

KATE   I know it is the sun that shines so bright.

PETRUCHIO   (*stopping*) Evermore crossed and crossed, nothing but crossed.

KATE   Forward, I pray, and be it moon or sun, or what you please –

PETRUCHIO   I say it is the moon.

KATE   I know it is the moon.

PETRUCHIO   Nay, then you lie. It is the blessed sun.

KATE   Then God be blessed, it is the blessed sun,
                 but sun it is not, when you say it is not,
                 and the moon changes even as your mind;
                 what you shall have it named, even that it
                 is, and so it shall be so for Katherine.

                 And so they come to Padua. Hortensio
                 marries his rich widow, and Bianca marries
                 her lover Lucentio. And afterwards, there is a
                 great banquet.

BAPTISTA   (*becoming maudlin*) Now, in good sadness,
                 son Petruchio, I think thou hast the veriest
                 shrew of all.

PETRUCHIO   Well, I say no. And therefore, for assurance,
                 let's each one send unto his wife, and he
                 whose wife is most obedient, shall win the
                 wager which we will propose.

HORTENSIO   Content. What's the wager?

LUCENTIO   Twenty crowns.

PETRUCHIO   Twenty crowns? I'll venture so much of
                 my hawk or hound, but twenty times so
                 much upon my wife!

LUCENTIO   A hundred then.

PETRUCHIO   A match! 'Tis done.

HORTENSIO   Who shall begin?

LUCENTIO   That will I. (*To servant*) Go, bid your
                      mistress come to me.

                      *The servant leaves, watched contentedly by
                      Lucentio and Baptista. Soon he returns.*

LUCENTIO   How now, what news?

SERVANT   Sir, my mistress sends you word that she is
                      busy, and she cannot come.

PETRUCHIO   How? 'She's busy, and she cannot come'?
                      Is that an answer?

GREMIO   Pray God, sir, your wife send you not
                      a worse!

HORTENSIO   (*to servant*) Go and entreat my wife to
                      come to me forthwith. (*The servant leaves
                      the room.*)

PETRUCHIO   O ho, entreat her! Nay, then she needs
                      must come!

HORTENSIO   I am afraid, sir, do what you can, yours
                      will not be entreated. (*The servant returns.*)

Now, where's my wife?

SERVANT   She will not come; she bids you come to her.

PETRUCHIO   Worse and worse; 'She will not come'! O vile, intolerable, not to be endured. (*To Grumio, his servant*) Go to your mistress, say I command her to come to me. (*Grumio departs.*)

HORTENSIO   I know her answer.

PETRUCHIO   What?

HORTENSIO   She will not.

Kate enters charmingly.

KATE   What is your will, sir, that you send for me?

PETRUCHIO   Where is your sister, and Hortensio's wife?

KATE   They sit conferring by the parlour fire.

PETRUCHIO   Away, I say, and bring them hither straight!

Kate leaves.

171

LUCENTIO

Here is a wonder, if you talk of wonder!

HORTENSIO

And so it is. I wonder what it bodes.

PETRUCHIO

Marry, peace it bodes, and love, and quiet life.

BAPTISTA

Now fair befall thee, good Petruchio! The wager thou hast won, and I will add unto their losses twenty thousand crowns, another dowry to another daughter, for she is changed, as she had never been!

PETRUCHIO

Nay, I will win my wager better yet. (*Kate enters, propelling the unwilling Bianca, now a grim and furious angel, and the widow.*) Katherine, that cap of yours becomes you not. Off with that bauble! (*Kate smiles, takes off the cap and treads on it.*)

WIDOW

Lord, let me never have cause to sigh till I be brought to such a silly pass!

BIANCA

Fie, what a foolish duty call you this?

LUCENTIO

I wish your duty were as foolish too! The wisdom of your duty, fair Bianca, hath cost me a hundred crowns since supper-time.

BIANCA

The more fool you for laying on my duty!

172

PETRUCHIO   Katherine, I charge thee tell these
                 headstrong women what duty they do owe
                 their lords and husbands.

WIDOW   She shall not!

KATE   (*with exaggeration, Petruchio finding it hard
                 to restrain himself from laughing at their
                 mutual joke*) Fie, fie, unknit that
                 threatening unkind brow. It blots thy
                 beauty. A woman moved is like a fountain
                 troubled, muddy, ill-seeming, thick, bereft
                 of beauty. Thy husband is thy lord, thy life,
                 thy keeper – one that cares for thee; and
                 for thy maintenance, commits his body to
                 painful labour both by sea and land, whilst
                 thou liest warm at home, secure and safe,
                 and craves no other tribute at thy hands
                 but love, fair looks, and true obedience –
                 too little payment for so great a debt.

                 *Kate lays her hands under her husband's feet
                 with a dramatic flourish and smiles
                 triumphantly up at him. He looks adoringly
                 at her.*

PETRUCHIO   Why, there's a wench! Come on, and kiss
                 me, Kate! (*She does so. He turns to
                 Lucentio.*) 'Twas I won the wager, and
                 being a winner, God give you good night!

173

(*They leave together, fondly entwined.*)

The play is over and Christopher Sly is fast asleep. The lord and his companions smile. The tinker's dream must end where it began.

Sly is carried back to the ale-house where he had been found and left propped against the tethering-post. He awakes.

SLY   Sim, gi's some more wine. What's all the players gone? (*He surveys his own wretched attire, and sadly shakes his head.*) Am I not a lord? (*He sighs, then he smiles.*) I have had the bravest dream. I know now how to tame a shrew.

He rises uncertainly, and totters into the ale-house with some determination. A moment latter, he comes out, a good deal more rapidly than he went in, followed by a hail of household utensils.

HOSTESS'S VOICE   A pair of stocks, you rogue!

The curtain falls.

Romeo and Juliet

This is the most famous love story in the world. Set in old Verona, where streets were narrow, walls were high and the sun was hot, and young men, bright as wasps, wore swords for their stings, it tells of a pair of lovers destroyed by the hatred of their rival families.

Shakespeare wrote it when he was about thirty-one. He took the story from a well-known poem of the time, and transformed it from a dull piece into a glittering marvel. Glittering is indeed the word: the play radiates light . . . not the light of the sun, but light that shines in darkness: torches, moon, stars and the lovers themselves. When Romeo first sees Juliet he declares, 'She doth teach the torches to burn bright', and when Juliet dreams of Romeo, she sighs, 'when he shall die, take him and cut him out in little stars, and he will make the face of heaven so fine that all the world will be in love with night.'

Although it is a tragedy, it is a play of almost as much laughter as tears; although it is a love story, it is a play of as many quarrels as kisses and as much fury as tenderness in its brief journey from the bedchamber to the tomb.

Some critics have complained that the play is no true tragedy, as the disaster that overwhelms the young lovers is brought about by chance – a letter that miscarries – and so is artificial and contrived. But this is not so. The tragedy is implicit from the very outset. Before Romeo sets eyes on Juliet, he has a premonition of ill-fortune, and when Juliet sees Romeo in the night she fancies him a dead man in a tomb; and even the kindly priest who marries them warns: 'These violent delights have violent ends, and in their triumph die.'

A tragic end is essential to Shakespeare's design. He tells the story of first love – a love so sudden, so bright, so intense that it cannot last. It is, as Juliet says, 'too like the lightning, that doth cease to be ere one can say it lightens.'

Had the lovers lived on, at best their bright flame would have sunk to a cosy glow; at worst, it would have turned to bitter ashes or mere forgetfulness. Death alone could preserve it in all its 'feasting presence full of light'. Life would have destroyed it; death has kept it bright for ever.

The Characters in the Play

in order of appearance

BENVOLIO	*Montague's nephew, friend to Romeo and Mercutio*
TYBALT	*Lady Capulet's nephew*
A CITIZEN	
CAPULET	*head of a Veronese family, at feud with the Montagues*
LADY CAPULET	
MONTAGUE	*head of a Veronese family, at feud with the Capulets*
LADY MONTAGUE	
ESCALUS	*Prince of Verona*
ROMEO	*Montague's son*
SERVANT	*to the Capulets*
MERCUTIO	*a young gentleman, kinsman of the Prince, friend of Romeo*
SERVANT	*at the masked ball*
JULIET	*Capulet's daughter*
NURSE	*a Capulet servant, Juliet's foster-mother*
FRIAR LAURENCE	*of the Franciscan order*
SERVANT	*of Romeo*
APOTHECARY	*of Mantua*
FRIAR JOHN	*of the Franciscan order*

The curtain rises on old Verona, on a market-place covered over with huge umbrella-awnings that shield the busy crowded stalls from the blazing summer's sun. All of a sudden, the umbrellas quake and tumble aside to reveal, like furious insects under a stone, a frantic squabbling of mad colours. Shouts and shrieks fill the air, of fright and rage and outrage! The Montagues and the Capulets – two ancient warring families – are at each others' throats again! Stalls are wrecked, merchandise scattered and screaming children snatched out of the way by their terrified mothers.

VOICES   Down with the Capulets! Down with the Montagues!

Benvolio, a sensible young Montague, seeks to put an end to the uproar.

BENVOLIO   Part, fools, put up your swords!

He is accosted by Tybalt, a dangerous Capulet.

TYBALT   Turn thee, Benvolio, look upon thy death!

They fight, causing more destruction to all about them.

A CITIZEN   A plague on both your houses!

Old Capulet, venerable and dignified, accompanied by his wife and a servant,

178

appears upon the scene. At once, the old man's heart is stirred into a fury.

CAPULET   Give me my long sword, ho!

LADY CAPULET   (*restraining him*) A crutch, a crutch! Why call you for a sword?

Too late. The old man has seen his chief enemy. Old Montague and his lady approach.

CAPULET   My sword, I say! Old Montague is come!

MONTAGUE   Thou villain Capulet!

He draws his sword, but Lady Montague drags him back.

MONTAGUE   Hold me not! Let me go!

LADY MONTAGUE   Thou shalt not stir one foot to seek a foe!

Trumpets sound. Soldiers and Prince Escalus enter the market-place. Enraged by the scene of civil strife that greets him, the prince shouts, at first, in vain.

PRINCE   Rebellious subjects, enemies to peace –
Will they not hear? What ho, you men, you
beasts! On pain of torture, throw your

mistempered weapons to the ground and hear the sentence of your moved prince. (*The fighting ceases.*) Three civil brawls, bred of an airy word, by thee, old Capulet, and Montague, have thrice disturbed the quiet of our streets. If ever you disturb our streets again, your lives shall pay the forfeit of the peace. For this time all the rest depart away.

At the Prince's words the crowd obediently disperses, leaving ruin and the creators of it behind. Sternly, the Prince addresses the two old men.

PRINCE

You, Capulet, shall go along with me, and Montague, come you this afternoon, to know our farther pleasure in this case.

He turns and rides away. Old Capulet and his wife follow, and with them, the sullen Tybalt. Angrily, Lady Capulet snatches his rapier away from him, as if depriving a naughty child of its toy. Old Montague, his wife and Benvolio are left behind with a stall-keeper or two, crawling about to recover scattered possessions.

LADY MONTAGUE

O where is Romeo, saw you him today?

BENVOLIO   Madam, underneath the grove of
                  sycamore did I see your son –

MONTAGUE   – Many a morning hath he there been
                  seen, with tears augmenting the fresh
                  morning's dew, adding to clouds more
                  clouds with his deep sighs . . .

BENVOLIO   My noble uncle, do you know the cause?

MONTAGUE   I neither know it, nor can learn it of him.

BENVOLIO   See where he comes!

                  *Enter Romeo, a sad figure, moving
                  disconsolately along a colonnade. He pauses
                  by a column and, with his dagger, begins to
                  incise in the stone.*

BENVOLIO   (*to Montague and his wife*) So please you
                  step aside; I'll know his grievance or be
                  much denied.

                  *Old Montague and his wife depart. Benvolio
                  approaches Romeo.*

BENVOLIO   Good morrow, cousin.

ROMEO   (*obscuring his knife-work*) What, is the day
                  so young?

BENVOLIO   But new struck nine.

ROMEO   Ay me, sad hours seem long.

BENVOLIO   What sadness lengthens Romeo's hours?

For answer, Romeo reveals what he has been hiding: the name, 'Rosalyne' with an added heart. All the columns he has passed have been similarly wounded by his loving dagger.

BENVOLIO   In love?

ROMEO   Out. Out of her favour where I am in love.

Benvolio seats himself upon a step, and signs to Romeo to join him.

BENVOLIO   Be ruled by me, forget to think of her.

ROMEO   O teach me how I should forget.

BENVOLIO   By giving liberty unto thine eyes: examine other beauties.

ROMEO   (*rising*) Farewell, thou canst not teach me –

As he speaks, a puzzled figure comes into the markét-place. It is a servant of the Capulets. He is studying a piece of paper. It is a list

*of guests invited to a feast at his master's
house. Unfortunately, he cannot read. He
approaches Romeo.*

SERVANT   I pray sir, can you read?

ROMEO   Ay, mine own fortune in my misery.

SERVANT   Perhaps you have learned it without book.

            He turns to go. Romeo detains him.

ROMEO   Stay, fellow, I can read. (*He takes the paper
            and begins to read.*)

ROMEO   Signor Martino and his wife and daughters;
            County Anselm and his beauteous sisters; the
            lady widow of Utruvio; Signor Placentio and
            his lovely nieces; Mercutio and his brother
            Valentine; mine uncle Capulet, his wife and
            daughters; my fair niece Rosalyne – (*Romeo
            pauses, then reads on*) – and Livia; Signor
            Valentio and his cousin Tybalt; Lucio and the
            lively Helena. (*He returns the list.*) A fair
            assembly. Whither should they come?

SERVANT   My master is the great rich Capulet, and if
            you be not of the house of Montagues, I
            pray come and crush a cup of wine. Rest
            you merry.

The servant departs with the list.

BENVOLIO

At this same ancient feast of Capulet's
sups the fair Rosalyne. Go thither and
with unattainted eye compare her face
with some that I shall show and I will
make thee think thy swan a crow.

ROMEO

One fairer than my love! The all-seeing
sun ne'er saw her match!

BENVOLIO

Tut, you saw her fair, none else
being by . . .

The house of the Capulets is noisy with revelry.
Gorgeous guests move to and fro. Masks, masks,
masks! In black and silver, scarlet and gold:
snarling beast-masks, beaked bird-masks, devil-
masks, and masks as pale and blank as the
moon . . . all shifting, turning, nodding, while
through their black slits peep eyes that burn and
sparkle and shoot voluptuous arrows of desire
. . . Old Capulet, the host, bustles about in
high delight.

CAPULET

Welcome, gentlemen, ladies that have their
toes unplagued with corns will walk a bout
with you . . . Come, musicians, play! A hall,
a hall, give room! And foot it, girls!

184

*A stately air strikes up. Couples form, beasts
and moon-faces . . . By the door stand Romeo
and Benvolio. Hastily, they don their masks.
Romeo's is calm and golden . . . Benvolio tries
to drag Romeo into the festivities. He will not
come. Mercutio, Romeo's good friend and
kinsman to the prince, in a mask that reflects
his lively, mocking nature, joins them. He lays
an affectionate arm round Romeo's shoulder.*

MERCUTIO   We must have you dance!

ROMEO   Not I, believe me. You have dancing shoes
                with nimble soles; I have a soul of lead.

MERCUTIO   You are a lover; borrow Cupid's wings!

ROMEO   Peace, peace, Mercutio, peace. (*Mercutio
                shrugs his shoulders and moves away. Romeo
                murmurs to himself.*) My mind misgives
                some consequence yet hanging in the stars
                shall bitterly begin his fearful date with
                this night's revels . . .

                *He gazes at the dancers: a long procession of
                pale moon-faces linked with lascivious beasts.
                Suddenly one face is seen unmasked. It is the
                face of a young girl and it seems to flood the
                world with radiance. Romeo cries out in
                amazement. He turns to a servant beside him.*

185

ROMEO	What lady's that which doth enrich the hand of yonder knight?
SERVANT	I know not, sir.
ROMEO	O she doth teach the torches to burn bright. It seems she hangs upon the cheek of night as a rich jewel in an Ethiop's ear! Did my heart love till now? Forswear it, sight, for I ne'er saw true beauty till this night!

He moves towards her like one in a dream. He passes close by Tybalt . . .

TYBALT	This by his voice should be a Montague! (*He turns to a serving-boy.*) Fetch me my rapier, boy! What, dares the slave come hither –

Old Capulet, seeing that Tybalt is enraged, approaches.

CAPULET	How now, kinsman, wherefore storm you so?
TYBALT	Uncle, this is a Montague, our foe!
CAPULET	Young Romeo, is it?
TYBALT	'Tis he, that villain Romeo.

186

CAPULET   Content thee, gentle coz, let him alone.

TYBALT   I'll not endure him!

CAPULET   He shall be endured! Go to, am I the master here or you? Go to, go to!

Old Capulet bustles away, leaving Tybalt to stare murderously towards Romeo. Romeo, unaware of the hostility he has aroused, has managed to obtain the unknown beauty as his partner in the dance. He takes her hand and holds up his mask.

ROMEO   If I profane with my unworthiest hand this holy shrine, the gentle sin is this, my lips, two blushing pilgrims, ready stand to smooth that rough touch with a tender kiss.

JULIET   Good pilgrim, you do wrong your hand too much, which mannerly devotion shows in this: saints have hands that pilgrims' hands do touch, and palm to palm is holy palmer's kiss.

ROMEO   Have not saints lips, and holy palmers too? (*Gently, and under the concealment of the mask, he kisses her.*) O trespass sweetly urged. Give me my sin again!

They kiss again.

JULIET   You kiss by th'book –

As they converse, lost in each other, Juliet's nurse, a busy, capacious dame approaches.

NURSE   Madam – (*hastily, the lovers' faces fly apart*) – your mother craves a word with you.

Obediently, Juliet departs.

ROMEO   What is her mother?

NURSE   Marry, bachelor, her mother is the lady of the house. I nursed her daughter that you talked withal. I tell you – (*she winks and digs Romeo in the ribs*) – he that can lay hold of her shall have the chinks. (*She bustles away.*)

ROMEO   Is she a Capulet? O dear account. My life is my foe's debt!

Aghast at this blow of fortune, Romeo disappears among the dancers. Juliet, having done with her mother, returns.

JULIET   Come hither, Nurse. What's he that is now going out of door?

NURSE	I know not. (*She speaks evasively.*)
JULIET	Go ask his name. If he be married, my grave is like to be my wedding bed.
NURSE	His name is Romeo, and a Montague, the only son of your great enemy.
JULIET	My only love sprung from my only hate! Too early seen unknown, and known too late!
NURSE	What's this? What's this?
JULIET	A rhyme I learned even now, of one I danced withal.
NURSE	(*leading Juliet away*) Anon, anon! Come let's away, the strangers are all gone!
	Night. The moon shines brightly on the orchard of the Capulets' house. There is a balcony, like a carved stone pocket, from which Juliet surveys the moonlight.
JULIET	O Romeo, Romeo, wherefore art thou Romeo? Deny thy father and refuse thy name . . . 'Tis but thy name that is my enemy; thou art thyself, though not a Montague. What's in a name? That which

we call a rose by any other word would
smell as sweet: so Romeo would, were he
not Romeo called. Romeo, doff thy name,
and for thy name, which is no part of thee,
take all myself.

*Suddenly, Romeo appears from the shadows
and stands below the balcony.*

ROMEO I take thee at thy word! Call me but love
and I'll be new baptised: henceforth I
never will be Romeo!

JULIET How cam'st thou hither? The orchard
walls are high and hard to climb –

ROMEO With love's light wings –

JULIET – And the place death, considering who
thou art, if any of my kinsmen find
thee here!

ROMEO Thy kinsmen are no stop to me!

JULIET If they do see thee, they will murder thee!

ROMEO Alack, there lies more peril in thine
eye than twenty of their swords! Look
thou but sweet and I am proof against
their enmity!

JULIET	Thou knowest the mask of night is on my face, else would a maiden blush bepaint my cheek for that which thou hast heard me speak tonight. Fain would I deny what I have spoke. But farewell, compliment. Dost thou love me? I know thou wilt say 'Ay', and I will take thy word. O gentle Romeo, if thou dost love, pronounce it faithfully –
ROMEO	Lady, by yonder blessed moon I vow –
JULIET	O swear not by the moon, the inconstant moon –
ROMEO	What shall I swear by?
JULIET	Do not swear at all.
ROMEO	If my heart's dear love –
JULIET	Well, do not swear. Although I joy in thee, I have no joy of this contract tonight: it is too rash, too unadvised, too sudden, too like the lightning, which doth cease to be ere one can say 'It lightens'. Sweet, good night.
ROMEO	O wilt thou leave me so unsatisfied?

JULIET	What satisfaction canst thou have tonight? I hear some noise within. Dear love, adieu.
NURSE'S VOICE	(*from within*) Madam.
JULIET	(*to Romeo*) Stay but a little, I will come again. (*She leaves the balcony for her room.*)
ROMEO	I am afeard, being in night, all this is but a dream.
	Juliet returns.
JULIET	Three words, dear Romeo, and good night indeed. If thy bent of love be honourable, thy purpose marriage, send me word tomorrow by one that I'll procure to come to thee, where and what time thou wilt perform the rite, and all my fortunes at thy foot I'll lay . . .
ROMEO	How silver-sweet sound lovers' tongues by night . . .
JULIET	What o'clock tomorrow shall I send to thee?
ROMEO	By the hour of nine.
NURSE	(*within*) Madam –

JULIET   Anon, good Nurse! Good night, good
night. Parting is such sweet sorrow that I
shall say good night till it be morrow.

*Morning. A busy street. Mercutio and
Benvolio are seeking Romeo, calling out
his name and shouting up at windows, to
the annoyance of those within, most of
all to the annoyance of the house of Rosalyne
where they strongly suspect Romeo
is concealed.*

MERCUTIO   Where the devil should this Romeo be?
Came he not home tonight?

BENVOLIO   Not to his father's; I spoke with his man.
Tybalt, the kinsman to old Capulet, hath
sent a letter to his father's house.

TYBALT   A challenge, on my life!

BENVOLIO   Romeo will answer it. Here comes Romeo!

Romeo enters, all dreamy softness and smiles.

MERCUTIO   You gave us the counterfeit fairly last night.

ROMEO   Good morrow to you both. What
counterfeit did I give you?

193

MERCUTIO   The slip, sir, the slip!

As they converse, the nurse appears, bustling along the street, preceded by her servant. She is a veritable galleon of a figure.

ROMEO   Here's goodly gear! A sail! A sail!

MERCUTIO   Two. Two. A shirt and a smock!

At once the three friends seize hold of the nurse and twirl her round and round. At length, the foolery subsides. The nurse is panting for breath.

NURSE   Out upon you! Gentlemen, can any of you tell me where I can find the young Romeo? (*Romeo bows in acknowledgement.*) If you be he, sir, I desire some confidence with you.

MERCUTIO   She will invite him to some supper.

Romeo waves his friends away. Mockingly, they bow as they depart.

MERCUTIO   Farewell, ancient lady, farewell . . .

NURSE   (*to Romeo*) Pray you, sir, a word – my young lady bid me enquire you out. What she bid me say, I will keep to myself. But first let me tell ye, if ye should lead her into a fool's paradise, as they say, it were a very gross behaviour, as they say; for the gentlewoman is young.

ROMEO   Nurse, commend me to thy lady and mistress. Bid her devise some means to come to shrift this afternoon, and there she shall at Friar Laurence's cell, be shrived and married.

NURSE   Now God in heaven bless thee. This afternoon, sir? Well, she shall be there.

In her apartment in the Capulets' house, Juliet waits impatiently for the return of the nurse, alternately pacing the floor and rushing to the window.

JULIET   The clock struck nine when I did send the Nurse, in half an hour she promised to return. Had she affections and warm youthful blood she would have been as swift in motion as a ball. But old folks, many feign as they were dead – unwieldy, slow, heavy, and pale as lead. O God she comes! (*She flies from the room to greet the nurse.*) O honey Nurse, what news? Hast thou met with him?

NURSE   Jesu, what haste. Can you not stay awhile?
                 Do you not see I am out of breath?

JULIET   How art thou out of breath to say thou art
                 out of breath? Is thy news good or bad?

NURSE   Lord, how my head aches –

JULIET   What says he of our marriage?

NURSE   O God's lady dear, are you so hot?

JULIET   Come, what says Romeo?

NURSE   Have you got leave to go to shrift today?

JULIET   I have.

NURSE   Then hie you hence to Friar Laurence's
                 cell. There stays a husband to make you
                 a wife.

                 *Juliet stares at the nurse, then embraces
                 her wildly.*

                 *Friar Laurence's cell. A plain, white-washed
                 room with an altar and crucifix above. The
                 window looks out upon a neat herb garden.
                 Romeo is waiting, in company with the friar,
                 a kindly old man in monkish habit.*

FRIAR   So smile the heavens on this holy act that
               after-hours with sorrow chide us not.

ROMEO   (*impatiently*) Amen, amen. Do thou but
               close our hands with holy words, then
               love-devouring death do what he dare –

FRIAR   These violent delights have violent ends –
               (*he glances through the window*) Here comes
               the lady.

               *Juliet enters, as if blown in by the summer
               breeze. At once, she and Romeo embrace.*

FRIAR   Come, come with me and we will make
               short work, for, by your leaves, you shall
               not stay alone till holy church incorporate
               two in one.

               *He leads them to the altar, where, side by side,
               they kneed before the friar.*

               *A street, in blazing sunshine, making the
               shadows sharp as knives. Mercutio and
               Benvolio are together.*

BENVOLIO   I pray thee, good Mercutio, let's retire;
               the day is hot, the Capel are abroad, and if
               we meet we shall not 'scape a brawl, for
               now, these hot days, is the mad blood

stirring. (*Even as he speaks, Tybalt and his followers appear.*) By my head, here comes the Capulets!

MERCUTIO   By my heel, I care not.

TYBALT   Gentlemen, good e'en: a word with one of you. Mercutio, thou consortest with Romeo.

MERCUTIO   Consort? What, dost thou make us minstrels?

              Mercutio's hand goes to his sword; but, at that moment, Romeo appears in the street. He walks as if on air. He is every inch the new-made bridegroom. He is holding a red rose, doubtless the late property of Juliet.

TYBALT   Peace be with you, sir, here comes my man. (*He addresses the rapturous Romeo.*) Boy, turn and draw. (*He flicks the flower from Romeo's hand with his rapier.*)

ROMEO   I do protest. I never injured thee, but love thee better than thou canst devise –

MERCUTIO   (*outraged*) O calm, dishonourable, vile submission! Tybalt, you ratcatcher! Will you walk?

TYBALT	I am for you! (*Tybalt and Mercutio begin to fight.*)
ROMEO	Gentlemen, for shame! Hold, Tybalt! Good Mercutio!
	He tries to pull Mercutio away. Tybalt lunges with his rapier, and pierces Mercutio. Mercutio cries out and Tybalt stares, amazed, at his blood-stained blade.
	The Capulets fly from the scene. Mercutio staggers. Romeo makes to support him. Mercutio pushes him away, angrily. He sinks to the ground.
MERCUTIO	I am hurt. A plague o' both your houses. I am sped. Is he gone and hath nothing?
ROMEO	What, art thou hurt?
MERCUTIO	Ay, ay, a scratch, a scratch. Marry, 'tis enough.
ROMEO	Courage, man, the hurt cannot be much.
MERCUTIO	No, 'tis not so deep as a well, nor so wide as a church door, but 'tis enough. Ask for me tomorrow and you shall find me a grave man. I am peppered, I warrant, for

199

this world. A plague o' both your houses. Why the devil came you between us? I was hurt under your arm.

ROMEO   I thought all for the best.

MERCUTIO   A plague o' both your houses! They have made worm's meat of me . . .

Mercutio dies. As Romeo looks down, shamed by his friend's reproach and grief-stricken by his death, a shadow falls across the body of Mercutio. Romeo looks up. Tybalt has returned. Enraged, Romeo draws his sword. They fight. Tybalt is killed. Romeo stares in horror at what he has done. A crowd begins to gather. Benvolio seizes Romeo by the arm.

BENVOLIO   Romeo, away, be gone! The Prince will doom thee to death!

ROMEO   O, I am fortune's fool!

Romeo flies for his life.

Night. Friar Laurence's cell. The door opens. The good friar enters, bearing a lantern that casts wild shadows.

FRIAR	Romeo, come forth, come forth, thou fearful man.

Romeo emerges palely from the shadows.

ROMEO	Father, what news? What is the Prince's doom?
FRIAR	A gentler judgement vanished from his lips: not body's death, but body's banishment. Hence from Verona art thou banished –
ROMEO	'Tis torture and not mercy! Heaven is here where Juliet lives, and every cat and dog and little mouse, every unworthy thing lives here in heaven and may look on her, but Romeo may not –
FRIAR	Thou fond mad man, hear me a little speak – (*There is a knocking on the door.*) Who's there?
NURSE'S VOICE	I come from Lady Juliet.

The nurse enters.

ROMEO	Nurse!
NURSE	Ah sir, ah sir, death's the end of all.

ROMEO Spak'st thou of Juliet? How is it with her?
Doth not she think me an old murderer
now I have stained the childhood of our
joy with blood removed but little from
her own?

NURSE O, she says nothing, sir, but weeps and
weeps, and now falls on her bed, and
then starts up, and Tybalt calls, and
then on Romeo cries, and then down
falls again.

Romeo draws his dagger as if to kill himself.

FRIAR Hold thy desperate hand. Go, get thee to
thy love as was decreed, ascend her
chamber – hence, and comfort her. But
look thou stay not till the Watch be set, for
then thou canst not pass to Mantua where
thou shalt live till we can find a time to
blaze your marriage, reconcile your
friends, beg pardon of the Prince and call
thee back . . .

NURSE Hie you, make haste, for it grows very late.

FRIAR Go hence, good night: either be gone
before the Watch is set, or by the break
of day . . .

Juliet's balcony. The night is giving way to a ragged grey dawn. A lark begins to sing. Romeo comes out of the bedchamber onto the balcony Juliet follows . . .

JULIET   Wilt thou be gone? It is not yet near day, it was the nightingale and not the lark –

ROMEO   It was the lark, the herald of the morn. Look, love, night's candles are burnt out, and jocund day stands tiptoe on the misty mountain tops. I must be gone and live, or stay and die.

JULIET   Yond light is not daylight, I know it –

ROMEO   Come death, and welcome. Juliet wills it so. It is not day –

JULIET   It is, it is. Hie hence, begone, away. It is the lark that sings to out of tune –

NURSE'S VOICE   Madam, your lady mother is coming to your chamber. The day is broke, be wary, look about.

Romeo and Juliet embrace passionately; then Romeo descends a rope ladder that hangs from the balcony.

ROMEO   Farewell, farewell.

                 Juliet stares down into the darkness in
                 which Romeo's face gleams palely, like a
                 drowned man.

JULIET   O think'st thou we shall ever meet again?

ROMEO   I doubt it not –

JULIET   O God, I have an ill-divining soul!
                 Methinks I see thee, now thou art so low,
                 as one dead in the bottom of a tomb.

ROMEO   Adieu, adieu!

                 With a last wave, he vanishes. Juliet stares
                 vainly for another glimpse of him. Lady
                 Capulet enters the bedchamber. Juliet hastily
                 leaves the balcony and returns inside.

LADY CAPULET   Why, how now, Juliet?

JULIET   Madam, I am not well.

LADY CAPULET   Evermore weeping for your cousin's
                 death? Well, well, thou hast a careful
                 father, child; one who to put thee from
                 heaviness hath sorted out a day of
                 sudden joy –

204

JULIET   What day is that?

LADY CAPULET   Marry, my child, early next Thursday
                morn the gallant, young and noble
                gentleman, the County Paris, at Saint
                Peter's Church, shall happily make thee
                there a joyful bride!

JULIET   (*aghast*) Now by Saint Peter's Church, and
                Peter too, he shall not make me there a
                happy bride! I will not marry yet. And
                when I do, I swear it shall be Romeo,
                whom you know I hate, rather than Paris –

LADY CAPULET   Here comes your father, tell him so
                yourself.

CAPULET   How now, wife, have you delivered to her
                our decree?

LADY CAPULET   Ay sir, but she will have none.

CAPULET   How? Will she none? Does she not give us
                thanks? (*He turns, furiously, upon his daughter*)
                Mistress minion you, but fettle your fine
                joints 'gainst Thursday next to go with Paris
                to Saint Peter's Church, or I will drag thee
                on a hurdle thither. Out, you green-sickness
                carrion! Out, you baggage!

JULIET	(*kneeling*) Good father, I beseech you –
CAPULET	Hang thee, young baggage, disobedient wretch! I tell thee what – get thee to church a Thursday or never after look me in the face! (*He storms out, followed by Lady Capulet.*)
JULIET	O God! – O Nurse, comfort me, counsel me!
NURSE	I think it best you married with the County. O, he's a lovely gentleman. Romeo's a dishclout to him.
JULIET	(*drawing away from the nurse and staring at her bitterly*) Well, thou hast comforted me marvellous much. Go in, and tell my lady I am gone, having displeased my father, to Laurence's cell, to make confession and be absolved.
NURSE	Marry, I will, and this is wisely done. (*She departs.*)
JULIET	Ancient damnation! O most wicked fiend! Thou and my bosom shall henceforth be twain. I'll to the Friar to know his remedy; if all else fail, myself have power to die.

In Friar Laurence's cell. Juliet kneels before the friar.

JULIET

God joined my heart and Romeo's, thou our hands; and ere this hand, by thee to Romeo sealed, or my true heart with treacherous revolt turn to another, this shall slay them both. (*She takes a dagger from her bosom.*)

FRIAR

Hold, daughter. I do spy a kind of hope. Go home, be merry, give consent to marry Paris. Wednesday is tomorrow; tomorrow night look that thou lie alone. Let not the Nurse lie with thee in thy chamber. (*He takes a small bottle from a shelf and gives it to her.*) Take thou this vial, being then in bed, and this distilling liquor drink thou off . . . Now when the bridegroom in the morning comes to rouse thee from thy bed, there thou art, dead. Then as the manner of our country is, in thy best robes, thou shalt be borne to that same ancient vault where all the kindred of the Capulets lie. In this borrowed likeness of shrunk death thou shalt continue two and forty hours and then awake as from a pleasant sleep. In the meantime, against thou shalt awake, shall Romeo by my letters know our drift and hither shall he come, and

he and I will watch thy waking, and that
very night shall Romeo bear thee hence
to Mantua.

Juliet nods and, clutching the vial, departs.
Hastily, Friar Laurence writes a letter and
summons Friar John, a brother of his order, to
take the letter to Romeo in Mantua.

A street in Mantua. Romeo waits, his eyes
never leaving the road that leads to Verona. A
horseman appears and rides towards him. It is
his servant.

ROMEO
News from Verona! How doth my lady? Is
my father well? How doth my Juliet? That
I ask again, for nothing can be ill if she
be well!

SERVANT
Then she is well and nothing can be ill.
Her body sleeps in Capels' monument.
I saw her laid low in her kindred's
vault, pardon me for bringing you these
ill news.

ROMEO
Is it e'en so? (*The servant nods.*) Then I
defy you, stars! I will hence tonight!

SERVANT
I do beseech you, sir, have patience!

ROMEO   Leave me. Hast thou no letters to me from
             the Friar?

SERVANT   None, my good lord.

ROMEO   No matter. Get thee gone. (*The servant
             leaves him.*) Well, Juliet, I will lie with thee
             tonight. Let's see for means. O mischief
             thou art swift to enter in the thoughts of
             desperate men. I do remember an
             apothecary . . .

             *The apothecary's shop. 'In his needy shop a
             tortoise hung, an alligator stuffed, and other
             skins of ill-shaped fishes; and about his shelves
             a beggarly account of empty boxes, green
             earthenware pots, bladders and musty seeds,
             remnants of packthread, and old cakes of
             roses . . .' Romeo enters, and the apothecary
             comes to attend him: 'in tattered weeds, with
             overwhelming brows.' Romeo leans upon the
             counter and beckons.*

ROMEO   Come hither, man. I see thou art poor.
             There is forty ducats. Let me have a dram
             of poison.

APOTHECARY   Such mortal drugs I have, but Mantua's
             law is death to any he that utters them.

ROMEO

Art thou so bare and full of wretchedness, and fear'st to die? The world is not thy friend, nor the world's law; the world affords no law to make thee rich; then be not poor, but break it, and take this. (*He pushes the money across the counter.*)

APOTHECARY

(*staring at the money*) My poverty, but not my will consents.

ROMEO

I pay thy poverty and not thy will.

The apothecary fumbles on his shelves and takes down a vial, which he lays on the counter. The withered hand of the apothecary and the fine white hand of Romeo cross: one takes the gold, the other, the poison.

ROMEO

I sell thee poison, thou hast sold me none. Farewell, buy food, get thyself in flesh.

He hastens from the shop.

Friar Laurence's cell. Friar Laurence looks up from his studies as Friar John enters.

FRIAR LAURENCE

Friar John, welcome from Mantua. What says Romeo?

Friar John gravely shakes his head.

FRIAR JOHN   Going to find a barefoot brother out, one
              of our order, to associate me, here in this
              city visiting the sick, and finding him,
              the searchers of the town, suspecting
              that we both were in a house where
              the infectious pestilence did reign,
              sealed up the doors and would not let us
              forth, so that my speed to Mantua there
              was stayed.

FRIAR LAURENCE   Who bare my letter then to Romeo?

FRIAR JOHN   I could not send it – here it is again –

FRIAR LAURENCE   Unhappy fortune! Now must I to the
              monument alone! Within these three hours
              will the fair Juliet wake!

              *In the utmost agitation, he leaves the cell;
              then, a moment later, returns for his lantern.
              He rushes forth again, and Friar John, full of
              guilt, watches Friar Laurence, lit by his
              lantern, whirl off into the dark . . .*

              *Within the monument of the Capulets. Juliet
              lies motionless on her bier, illuminated by four
              tall candles. About her, in the shadowy gloom,
              lie broken coffins on shelves . . . some with
              bones protruding and skulls peeping
              inquisitively forth, as if to welcome their fair*

new neighbour. Romeo enters. He approaches Juliet, and kneels beside her.

ROMEO   O my love, my wife! Death that hath sucked the honey of thy breath hath had no power upon thy beauty yet. Thou art not conquered. Beauty's ensign yet is crimson on thy lips and in thy cheeks, and Death's pale flag is not advanced there. Here, here will I remain with worms that are thy chambermaids; O here will I set up my everlasting rest . . . Eyes look your last! Arms take your last embrace! And lips, O you the doors of breath, seal with a righteous kiss a dateless bargain with engrossing Death!

He kisses Juliet, then holds up the vial of poison like a glass of wine.

ROMEO   Here's to my love! (*He drinks.*) O true Apothecary, thy drugs are quick!

He kisses Juliet again, then dies. A moment later, Friar Laurence enters the tomb. He gazes in despair at the scene. Slowly, Juliet stirs. She sees the friar.

JULIET   O comfortable Friar, where is my lord? (*She stares about her at the images of death*

212

and decay.) I do remember well where I should be, and there I am. Where is my Romeo?

FRIAR   I hear some noise. Lady, come from that nest of death, contagion, and unnatural sleep. A greater power than we can contradict hath thwarted our intents. Come, come away! Thy husband in thy bosom there lies dead. Come, I'll dispose of thee among a sisterhood of holy nuns. Stay not to question, for the Watch is coming. Come, go, good Juliet. I dare no longer stay.

JULIET   (*with quiet dignity*) Go, get thee hence, for I will not away.

The friar, wringing his hands in grief and dismay, departs. Juliet rises, and kneels beside the dead Romeo. She takes his hand and discovers the vial, still clutched in it.

JULIET   What's here? A cup closed in my true love's hand? Poison, I see, hath been his timeless end. (*She takes it, and sees it to be empty.*) O churl. Drunk all, and left no friendly drop to help me after? I will kiss thy lips. Haply some poison yet doth hang

on them. (*She kisses him.*) Thy lips are
warm –

*There are sounds of people approaching:
shouts and cries as they approach the tomb.*

JULIET   Yea, a noise? Then I'll be brief. (*She takes
Romeo's dagger.*) O happy dagger. This is
thy sheath. There rust, and let me die. (*She
stabs herself and falls lifeless into the arms of
the dead Romeo.*)

*Figures come crowding into the tomb,
flourishing torches. Among the awed faces are
old Capulet and Montague. Then comes the
Prince. He surveys the tragic scene, and turns
to the bereaved parents.*

PRINCE   Capulet, Montague, see what a scourge is
laid upon your hate, that heaven finds
means to kill your joys with love . . .

CAPULET   O brother Montague, give me thy hand.
This is my daughter's jointure, for no
more can I demand.

MONTAGUE   But I can give thee more, for I will raise
her statue in pure gold, that whiles Verona
by that name is known, there shall no

figure at such rate be set as that of true
and faithful Juliet.

CAPULET   As rich shall Romeo's by his lady lie, poor
sacrifices to our enmity.

*The curtain falls, not on the darkness of the
lovers' tomb, but on the brightness of it.*

As You Like It

As You Like It tells a story that begins in the discord and violence of a tyrant's court, where broken ribs and brotherly hatred are the orders of the day, and moves to the strange, enchanted Forest of Arden, where all wounds are healed and all ills made good, where the very trees sprout love-poems . . . It is a forest fairly infested with wandering lovers and outlaws who 'live like the old Robin Hood of England . . . and fleet the time carelessly, as they did in the golden world.'

It is indeed a golden play, and at the very heart of it is Rosalind, a banished princess, who, with her companions in exile, seeks the young Orlando, who, as her cousin puts it, 'tripped up the wrestler's heels, and your heart, both in an instant!'

216

The Characters in the Play

in order of appearance

DUKE FREDERICK	*usurper of Duke Senior*
ROSALIND	*daughter to Duke Senior*
CHARLES	*Duke Frederick's wrestler*
ORLANDO	*son of Sir Rowland de Boys*
CELIA	*daughter to Duke Frederick*
OLIVER	*son of Sir Rowland de Boys*
DUKE SENIOR	*living in exile*
LORD	*attending on Duke Senior*
ADAM	*an old servant of Sir Rowland de Boys*
TOUCHSTONE	*a Fool at Duke Frederick's court*
CORIN	*an old shepherd*
SILVIUS	*a shepherd*
AMIENS	*a lord attending Duke Senior*
JAQUES	*a lord attending Duke Senior*
AUDREY	*a goat-herd*
PHEBE	*a shepherdess*
HYMEN	*the god of marriage*
MESSENGER	

*Lords, servants and other attendants,
shepherds and shepherdesses*

The curtain rises on a lawn before the palace. There is to be a wrestling match before Duke Frederick and all his court. Already Charles, the strongest man in the country, has broken the ribs of three young men; now a fourth is awaited. Celia, the daughter of the duke, and Rosalind her cousin enter. They are followed by the duke and his courtiers, together with Charles the wrestler and Orlando, the fourth young man.

DUKE   How now, daughter and Rosalind? Are you crept hither to see the wrestling?

ROSALIND   Ay, uncle, so please you give us leave.

DUKE   You will take little delight in it, I can tell you, there is such odds in the man. In pity of the challenger's youth I would fain dissuade him, but he will not be entreated.

                Duke Frederick gives a sign and Charles and Orlando begin to wrestle. The girls exclaim while watching.

ROSALIND   Now Hercules be thy speed, young man!

CELIA   I would I were invisible, to catch the strong fellow by the leg!

                Charles is thrown.

ROSALIND	O excellent young man!
	Shouts of amazement and admiration. Only one man hides himself angrily in the crowd – Oliver, Orlando's brother, who hates him.
DUKE	(*to Orlando*) What is thy name, young man?
ORLANDO	Orlando, my liege, the youngest son of Sir Rowland de Boys.
DUKE	I would thou hadst been son to some man else; the world esteem'd thy father honourable, but I did find him still mine enemy.
	The duke departs barely suppressing his anger, followed by his court. Rosalind and Celia remain with Orlando.
CELIA	My father's rough and envious disposition sticks me at the heart. (*They approach Orlando.*)
ROSALIND	(*giving him a chain from her neck*) Gentleman, wear this for me; one out of suits with Fortune, that could give more, but that her hand lacks means.

Orlando is tongue-tied. Plainly, he and Rosalind
have fallen in love. Celia leads Rosalind away.
Orlando gazes after them, enraptured.

Rosalind and Celia are together in their
apartment.

CELIA   Come, come, wrestle with thy affections.

The duke enters furiously.

DUKE   Mistress, dispatch you with your safest
haste, and get you from our court!

ROSALIND   Me, uncle?

DUKE   You, cousin. Within these ten days if that
thou be'st found so near our public court as
twenty miles, thou diest for it!

ROSALIND   I do beseech your Grace, let me the
knowledge of my fault bear with me.

DUKE   Thou art thy father's daughter,
there's enough.

He storms out.

CELIA   O my poor Rosalind, whither wilt thou go?
Wilt thou change fathers? I will give thee

mine. Say what thou canst, I'll go along
with thee.

ROSALIND   Why, whither shall we go?

CELIA   To seek my uncle in the forest of Arden.

ROSALIND   Alas, what danger will it be to us? (*An idea
seems to have struck Rosalind . . .*) But what if
we assay'd . . .

*Eagerly, they dress themselves for their
adventure; Celia as a country maiden and
Rosalind as a youth. They persuade Touchstone,
the duke's jester, to bear them company in
the forest.*

CELIA   What shall I call thee when thou art a man?

ROSALIND   (*coming back in and putting on a hat*) Call me
Ganymede. But what will you be called?

CELIA   (*coming in and putting on an apron*) No
longer Celia, but Aliena.

*In the forest of Arden Rosalind's father, once
duke, but driven out by his younger brother
Frederick, lives in banishment with a few
faithful friends.*

221

DUKE SENIOR   Now my brothers in exile, hath not old custom made this life more sweet than that of painted pomp? Are not these woods more free from peril than the envious court? And this our life finds tongues in trees, books in the running brooks, and good in everything. Where is Jaques?

LORD   We today did steal behind him as he lay under an oak, to which place a poor stag, that from the hunter's aim had ta'en a hurt, did come to languish. He swears that we are mere usurpers, tyrants, and what's worse, fright the animals and kill them in their native dwelling-place.

DUKE SENIOR   Show me the place. I love to hear him in these sullen fits.

The duke and lords ride off.

Orlando returns to his home and finds Adam, his old servant, waiting for him at the door.

ADAM   O unhappy youth, come not within these doors! Your brother hath heard your praises, and this night he means to burn the lodging where you use to lie, and you within it.

ORLANDO

Why, whither, Adam, wouldst thou have me go? Wouldst thou have me go and beg my food? Or with a base and boist'rous sword enforce a thievish living on the common road?

ADAM

But do not so! I have five hundred crowns I saved under your father. Take that.

ORLANDO

O good old man.

ADAM

Let me go with you. Though I look old, yet I am strong and lusty.

ORLANDO

Come, we'll go along together.

The three travellers, Rosalind, Celia and Touchstone, limp miserably through the forest. Rosalind, being dressed as a man, feels it her duty to present a bold and cheerful appearance.

ROSALIND

Well, this is the forest of Arden.

TOUCHSTONE

Ay, now am I in Arden, the more fool I. When I was at home, I was in a better place.

ROSALIND

Look you, who comes here.

They withdraw into concealment as Corin, an old shepherd and Silvius enter.

SILVIUS   O Corin, that thou knew'st how I do love her!

CORIN   I partly guess; for I have loved ere now.

SILVIUS   No, Corin, being old, thou canst not guess.
O Phebe, Phebe, Phebe!

Silvius wanders away, distracted.

ROSALIND   Jove, Jove! This shepherd's passion is much
upon my fashion! (*Rosalind leaves the shelter
of the trees and approaches Corin.*) Good even
to you, friend.

CORIN   And to you, gentle sir, and to you all.

ROSALIND   I prithee, shepherd, bring us where we may
rest ourselves and feed. Here's a young maid
with travel much oppress'd, and faints
for succour.

CORIN   Fair sir, I pity her; but I am shepherd to
another man. His cottage, flocks, and
bounds of feed are now on sale, and there is
nothing that you will feed on –

ROSALIND   I pray thee, if it stands with honesty, buy
            thou the cottage, pasture, and the flock, and
            thou shalt have to pay for it of us.

CELIA   And we will mend thy wages.

CORIN   I will your very faithful feeder be.

            *Another part of the forest. Orlando appears,
            assisting his old servant.*

ADAM   Dear master, I can go no further. O, I die for
            food. Here lie I down and measure out my
            grave. Farewell, kind master.

ORLANDO   Why, how now, Adam? No greater heart in
            thee? Live a little, comfort a little, cheer
            thyself a little. If this uncouth forest yield
            anything savage, I will be either food for it,
            or bring it for food to thee.

            *Orlando unsheaths his sword and goes further
            into the forest. Hearing rustling in the grass, he
            stops and hides behind the bushes. A hound runs
            out and then runs deeper into the forest.
            Orlando follows the dog. He hears a song in
            the distance.*

AMIENS   Under the greenwood tree
                Who loves to lie with me,

And turn his merry note
Unto the sweet bird's throat,
Come hither, come hither, come hither!
Here shall he see
No enemy
But winter and rough weather.

*He follows the 'Come hither', towards a
glimmering of lights and creeps to look between
the foliage. The scene before him is of a banquet,
lantern lit, and surrounded by gentlemen in
comfortable furs. Among them is the melancholy
Jaques. A hound lies at the feet of Duke Senior.
The duke is about to sip from a goblet when he
is interrupted.*

ORLANDO   (*rushing forward with drawn sword*) Forbear,
and eat no more!

JAQUES   Why, I have eat none yet.

ORLANDO   Nor shalt not, till necessity be served.

DUKE SENIOR   Sit down and feed, and welcome to
our table.

ORLANDO   (*putting up his sword*) Speak you so gently?
Pardon me, I pray you. I thought that all
things had been savage here. There is an old
poor man –

226

DUKE SENIOR   Go find him out, and we will nothing waste till your return.

ORLANDO   (*departing*) I thank ye.

DUKE SENIOR   Thou seest we are not all alone unhappy: this wide and universal theatre presents more woeful pageants than the scene wherein we play.

JAQUES   All the world's a stage and all the men and women merely players. They have their exits and their entrances, and one man in his time plays many parts, his acts being seven ages. At first the infant . . . then the whining schoolboy . . . and then the lover. Then a soldier, jealous in honour, sudden, and quick in quarrel, and then the justice. The sixth age shifts into the lean and slipper'd pantaloon, with spectacles on nose. Last scene of all that ends this history, is second childishness, sans teeth, sans eyes, sans taste, sans everything.

As Jaques finishes his monologue, Orlando returns with Adam who is warmly welcomed, as if in contradiction of Jaques' grim view of old age.

At the palace, Duke Frederick discovers his daughter's flight with Rosalind; and, having heard of their talk with Orlando, suspects that they have all fled together. In a rage, he sends for Oliver, and orders him to find his brother Orlando or risk banishment himself.

In the forest Orlando has decorated all the trees he can find with poems of love to Rosalind.

ORLANDO   Hang there my verse, in witness of my love.

And away he goes in search of still more trees. No sooner has he gone than Rosalind appears with a poem in her hand.

ROSALIND   'From the east to western Inde,
No jewel is like Rosalind.
All the pictures fairest lin'd
Are but black to Rosalind.
Let no face be kept in mind
But the fair of Rosalind'.

Enter Celia, with another poem.

CELIA   'Thus Rosalind of many parts,
By heavenly synod was devis'd,
Of many faces, eyes, and hearts . . .'

TOUCHSTONE   *(peeping out from behind a tree)* This is the

228

very false gallop of verses; why do you infect
yourself with them?

ROSALIND   Peace, you dull fool! I found them on a tree.

TOUCHSTONE   Truly, the tree yields bad fruit.

*He disappears. Celia holds out her paper
to Rosalind.*

CELIA   Trow you who hath done this?

ROSALIND   Is it a man?

CELIA   It is young Orlando that tripped up the
wrestler's heels and your heart, both in
an instant.

ROSALIND   Alas the day, what shall I do with my
doublet and hose? How looked he?

CELIA   Soft, comes he not here?

*They retire into concealment. Orlando and
Jaques appear.*

JAQUES   Rosalind is your love's name?

ORLANDO   Yes, just.

JAQUES   I do not like her name.

ORLANDO   There was no thought of pleasing you when
                she was christened.

JAQUES   What stature is she of?

ORLANDO   Just as high as my heart.

JAQUES   You are full of pretty answers. Farewell,
                good Signior Love.

                *Jaques goes off in disgust. Rosalind leans
                forward. Orlando is whittling a boat.*

ROSALIND   I pray you, what is't o'clock?

ORLANDO   You should ask me what time o'day. There is
                no clock in the forest.

                *He puts his boat into the brook. A sheet with verses
                is the sail. Rosalind throws a pebble at the boat.*

ORLANDO   (*angrily*) What would you?

ROSALIND   (*jumps down from her branch and points to a
                tree carved with 'Rosalind'*) There is a man
                haunts the forest, that abuses our young
                plants, hangs odes upon hawthorns and
                elegies on brambles, all deifying the name of

Rosalind. If I could meet that fancy-monger, I would give him some good counsel.

ORLANDO   I am he that is so love-shaked.

ROSALIND   Love is merely a madness; yet I profess curing it by counsel.

ORLANDO   Did you ever cure any so?

ROSALIND   Yes, one, and in this manner. He was to imagine me his love, his mistress; and I set him every day to woo me. At which time would I grieve, be proud, fantastical, apish, inconstant, full of tears, full of smiles, that I drave my suitor from his mad humour of love to a living humour of madness. And thus I cured him.

ORLANDO   I would not be cured, youth.

ROSALIND   I would cure you, if you would but call me Rosalind, and come every day to my cote and woo me.

Love grows in the forest fast as weeds. Even Touchstone has found himself a mate, and being of the spirit, he has mocked even himself with his choice. He has found a true country lass, as thick as mud.

TOUCHSTONE	I will fetch up your goats, Audrey, as another poet did. Truly, I wish the gods had made thee poetical.
AUDREY	I do not know what 'poetical' is. Is it honest?
TOUCHSTONE	No truly; for the truest poetry is the most feigning.
AUDREY	Well, I am not fair, and therefore I pray the gods make me honest.
TOUCHSTONE	Truly, and to cast away honesty upon a foul slut were to put good meat into an unclean dish. But be it as it may be, I will marry thee.

Nearby their cottage, Rosalind and Celia await Orlando. He is late.

ROSALIND	Never talk to me, I will weep.
CELIA	Do, but consider that tears do not become a man.
ROSALIND	Why did he swear he would come this morning, and comes not?
CELIA	Nay certainly there is no truth in him.

ROSALIND	Not true in love? You have heard him swear he was.
CELIA	'Was' is not 'is'.

Old Corin approaches.

CORIN	Mistress and master, you have oft enquired after the shepherd that complained of love –
CELIA	Well, and what of him?

Corin, with his finger to his lips, beckons. They creep forward, part some foliage and observe Silvius and his Phebe.

SILVIUS	Sweet Phebe, do not scorn me, do not Phebe! If ever you meet in some fresh cheek the power of fancy, then shall you know the wounds invisible that love's keen arrows make.
PHEBE	But till that time, come not thou near me; and when that time comes, afflict me with thy mocks, pity me not, as till that time, I shall not pity thee.
SILVIUS	Oh!

ROSALIND (*coming forward*) And why, I pray you? Who might be your mother, that you insult, exult, and all at once, over the wretched? You foolish shepherd, wherefore do you follow her? Mistress, know yourself. Down on your knees, and thank heaven fasting for a good man's love; for I must tell you friendly in your ear, sell when you can, you are not for all markets.

PHEBE Sweet youth, I pray you chide a year together, I had rather hear you chide than this man woo.

ROSALIND I pray you do not fall in love with me, for I am falser than vows made in wine.
(*She leaves.*)

PHEBE (*gazing after Rosalind*) Who ever loved that loved not at first sight?

In another part of the forest. Rosalind is standing on a bridge across the brook. At last, Orlando arrives.

ORLANDO My fair Rosalind, I come within an hour of my promise.

ROSALIND Break an hour's promise in love!

ORLANDO   Pardon me, dear Rosalind.

ROSALIND   Nay, and you be so tardy, come no more in my sight. I had as lief been wooed of a snail. Am not I your Rosalind?

ORLANDO   I would take some joy to say you are, because I would be talking of her.

ROSALIND   Well, in her person, I say I will not have you.

ORLANDO   Then in mine own person, I die.

ROSALIND   No, faith, men have died from time to time, and worms have eaten them, but not for love. But come now, I will be your Rosalind in a more coming-on disposition; and ask me what you will, I will grant it.

ORLANDO   Then love me, Rosalind.

ROSALIND   Ay, and twenty such. Now tell me how long you would have her after you have possessed her.

ORLANDO   For ever and a day.

ROSALIND   Say 'a day' without the 'ever'. No, no, Orlando, men are April when they woo, December when they wed; maids are May

when they are maids, but the sky changes
when they are wives.

ORLANDO   But will my Rosalind do so?

ROSALIND   By my life, she will do as I do.

The sound of a horn is heard.

ORLANDO   I must attend the duke at dinner. For these
two hours I will leave thee. Adieu.

He departs. Celia appears from behind a tree.

CELIA   You have simply misused our sex in your
love-prate.

ROSALIND   (*taking off her hat, fluffing out her hair, and
lying on the grass*) O coz, coz, coz, my pretty
little coz, that thou didst know how many
fathom deep I am in love!

*There is yet another victim of Duke Frederick's
fury in the forest. Oliver de Boys, sent to fetch
his brother, has wandered, lost and wretched, till
at last he lies down to rest. As he sleeps, a lioness
approaches. Then it is that Orlando, coming
upon his brother, and seeing his danger, fights
with the lioness and overcomes it. But in so
doing, Orlando is wounded himself. Faint from*

236

loss of blood, he sends Oliver to keep his
appointment with the shepherd boy. All enmity
between the brothers is now ended.

OLIVER   Good morrow, fair ones. Orlando doth
           commend him to you both. He sent me
           hither, stranger as I am, to tell this story,
           that you might excuse his broken promise,
           and to give this napkin, dy'd in his blood,
           unto the shepherd youth that he in sport
           doth call his Rosalind.

           He holds out the napkin. Rosalind faints.

CELIA   Why, how now, Ganymede, sweet
           Ganymede?

           Celia and Oliver rush to help Rosalind up, but
           bump their heads together and, blushing, stare at
           each other.

OLIVER   Many will swoon when they do look
           on blood.

ROSALIND   I would I were at home.

           They help her back to the cottage.

           There is a haystack in a clearing. Voices come
           from it.

TOUCHSTONE	We shall find a time, Audrey, patience, gentle Audrey.
CORIN	(*entering and knocking on the haystack*) Our master and mistress seeks you. Come away, away!
TOUCHSTONE	(*to Audrey, who has run out and is putting herself in order*) Trip, Audrey, trip Audrey! I attend, I attend.

A clearing in the forest. Oliver and Orlando are together. Orlando's arm is in a sling.

ORLANDO	Is't possible that on so little acquaintance you should like her?
OLIVER	I love Aliena; she loves me; consent with both that we may enjoy each other. My father's house and all the revenue that was old Sir Rowland's will I estate upon you, and here live and die a shepherd.
ORLANDO	Let your wedding be tomorrow; thither will I invite the duke and all's contented followers.

Off goes Oliver, delighted. Rosalind appears.

ROSALIND   O my dear Orlando, how it grieves me to see
               thee wear thy heart in a scarf.

ORLANDO   It is my arm.

ROSALIND   Did your brother tell you how well I
               counterfeited to swoon when he showed me
               your handkercher?

ORLANDO   Ay, and greater wonders than that.

ROSALIND   O, I know where you are. Nay, 'tis true. Your
               brother and my sister are in the very wrath
               of love.

ORLANDO   They shall be married tomorrow. But O,
               how bitter a thing it is to look into happiness
               through another man's eyes!

ROSALIND   Why then tomorrow I cannot serve your
               turn for Rosalind?

ORLANDO   I can no longer live by thinking.

ROSALIND   (*mysteriously*) I can do strange things. Put
               you in your best array, bid your friends; for if
               you will be married tomorrow, you shall;
               and to Rosalind, if you will.

               Silvius and Phebe appear.

PHEBE   Youth, you have done me much
             ungentleness –

ROSALIND   I care not if I have. You are there followed by
             a faithful shepherd – look upon him, love
             him; he worships you.

PHEBE   Good shepherd, tell this youth what 'tis
             to love.

SILVIUS   It is to be all made of sighs and tears, and so
             am I for Phebe.

PHEBE   And I for Ganymede.

ORLANDO   And I for Rosalind.

ROSALIND   And I for no woman.

SILVIUS   It is to be all made of faith and service, and
             so am I for Phebe.

PHEBE   And I for Ganymede.

ORLANDO   And I for Rosalind.

ROSALIND   And I for no woman.

SILVIUS   It is to be all made of fantasy, all made
             of passion –

ROSALIND

Pray you no more of this, 'tis like the howling of Irish wolves against the moon! (*To Phebe*) I will marry you if ever I marry woman, and I'll be married tomorrow. But if you do refuse to marry me, you'll give yourself to this most faithful shepherd.

PHEBE

So is the bargain.

ROSALIND

Keep your word; from hence I go to make these doubts all even. Tomorrow meet me all together.

The morning sun breaks through into a clearing. A flute plays. Duke Senior, Jaques, Orlando, Oliver and Celia are waiting.

AMIENS

(*singing*) It was a lover and his lass,
    With a hey and a ho and a hey nonino,
    That o'er the green corn-field did pass,
    In spring-time, the only pretty ring-time,
    When birds do sing, hey ding a ding, ding,
    Sweet lovers love the spring.

DUKE SENIOR

Dost thou believe, Orlando, that Ganymede can do all this that he hath promised?

ORLANDO

I sometimes do believe, and sometimes do not.

241

Touchstone and Audrey, Silvius and Phebe enter.

JAQUES   There is sure another flood toward, and these couples are coming to the ark.

TOUCHSTONE   I press in here, sir, to swear and forswear, according as marriage binds and blood breaks. (*Pushing Audrey forward*) A poor virgin, sir, an ill-favoured thing, sir, but mine own.

Hymen enters.

HYMEN   Good Duke, receive thy daughter,
Hymen from heaven brought her,
That thou mightst join her hand with his
Whose heart within his bosom is.

He beckons and Rosalind, now dressed as herself, appears.

ROSALIND   (*to Duke*) To you I give myself, for I am yours. (*To Orlando*) To you I give myself for I am yours.

DUKE SENIOR   If there be truth in sight, you are my daughter.

ORLANDO   If there be truth in sight, you are my Rosalind.

242

PHEBE   If sight and shape be true, why then my
                 love adieu!

HYMEN   Here's eight that must take hands,
                 To join in Hymen's bands.
                 (*To Orlando and Rosalind*)
                 You and you no cross shall part.
                 (*To Oliver and Celia*)
                 You and you are heart in heart.
                 (*To Phebe*)
                 You to his love must accord,
                 Or have a woman for your lord.
                 (*To Touchstone and Audrey*)
                 You and you are sure together,
                 As the winter to foul weather.
                 The couples embrace. A messenger enters.

MESSENGER   Let me have audience for a word or two.
                 Duke Frederick addressed a mighty
                 power to take his brother here, and to
                 the skirts of this wild wood he came.
                 Meeting with an old religious man, he was
                 converted from his enterprise and from the
                 world, his crown bequeathing to his
                 banished brother.

DUKE SENIOR   Every of this happy number that have
                 endur'd shrewd days and nights with us,
                 shall share the good of our returned
                 fortune . . . Play, music, and you brides and

bridegrooms all, with measure heap'd in joy,
to th' measures fall!

As the curtain falls, the couples pass before the spectators in joyful dancing.

Hamlet

More books have been written about *Hamlet* than about any other story ever told: for Hamlet is Everyman, who questions the very reason for his own existence: 'To be, or not to be . . .' Set in Denmark, long ago, it is a tale of revenge; of a prince who is called upon, by the ghost of his dead father, to avenge his father's murder by the hand of his uncle, who is now the king.

Shakespeare took the story from the work of an old Danish historian, and, like all his borrowings, the debt was repaid a thousandfold. He takes pebbles, as was said of the composer Handel, and gives back diamonds.

Shakespeare wrote it, probably, when he was about thirty-seven or thirty-eight; but the date, like everything else in this play, is uncertain. Doubt and mystery stalk its pages, like the ghost that stalks the battlements. Is the ghost an 'honest ghost', or is it a 'goblin damned'? Does the queen know of her husband's crime, or is she, like others, an innocent victim? And at the very heart of things is Prince Hamlet himself – surely the most brilliant and complex character ever put upon the stage! Although he tells us what is in his mind, we never truly know what is in his heart. 'You would pluck out the heart of my mystery,' he accuses a seeming friend; and then denies the possibility of any such thing: 'You can fret me, you cannot play upon me.'

For many, many years now, scholars, poets and psychologists have fretted at Hamlet; but the brooding, black-clad prince somehow eludes them all. Why does he delay in his revenge? He does not seem to know himself. Time and again he asks himself that question, and the only answer he can provide is that he thinks too much: 'the native hue of resolution is sicklied o'er with the pale cast of thought.'

A strange hero; yet one who lives in the mind like no other: a pale young man standing on the battlements of an ancient castle, under a night sky, crying out bitterly, as if to an unjust God, 'the time is out of joint: O cursed spite that ever I was born to set it right.'

The Characters in the Play

in order of appearance

MARCELLUS	*members of the King's guard*
BARNADO	
GHOST	*of the late King, Hamlet's father*
HORATIO	*friend and confidant of Hamlet*
HAMLET	*Prince of Denmark*
CLAUDIUS	*King of Denmark, Hamlet's uncle*
LAERTES	*Polonius' son*
POLONIUS	*a councillor of state*
GERTRUDE	*the Queen, Hamlet's mother, now wife of Claudius*
OPHELIA	*Polonius' daughter*
(THE PLAYER KING)	*players*
(THE PLAYER QUEEN)	
(MURDERER)	
SOLDIER	
GRAVEDIGGER	
COURTIER	
JUDGE	
SERVANT	

(Names in brackets indicate non-speaking parts)

The curtain rises on the battlements of a dark and forbidding castle. It is night. Three figures are huddled together. They are Marcellus and Barnardo, sentinels, and Horatio, a visitor to the castle. They are staring fearfully about them.

MARCELLUS   Look where it comes again!

Out of the swirling nothingness comes a ghostly figure, all in armour. Slowly it stalks by; and its face, seen beneath its helmet, is filled with gloom.

BARNARDO   In the same figure like the king that's dead!

MARCELLUS   Is it not like the king, Horatio?

HORATIO   As thou art to thyself. (*The apparition vanishes.*) Let us impart what we have seen unto young Hamlet.

They all stare after the vanished phantom.

MARCELLUS   Something is rotten in the state of Denmark.

In the royal council chamber, the king and queen sit fondly side by side. Behind them stands Polonius, the doting old Lord Chamberlain. The brightly coloured court looks smiling on. But one figure sits apart, and all in black. It is Prince Hamlet. He stares at his mother, the queen, then turns away.

248

HAMLET   (*to himself*) That it should come to this! A
          little month, or ere those shoes were old with
          which she followed my poor father's body – O
          God, a beast that wants discourse of reason
          would have mourned longer! – married to my
          uncle, my father's brother, but no more like
          my father than I to Hercules!

          *As he murmurs to himself, a young man of the
          court comes and kneels before the king.*

KING   What wouldst thou beg, Laertes?

LAERTES   My dread lord, your leave and favour to
          return to France.

KING   Have you your father's leave? What
          says Polonius?

POLONIUS He hath, my lord, wrung from me my
          slow leave.

KING   Take thy fair hour, Laertes. (*Laertes bows and
          withdraws.*) But now my cousin Hamlet, and
          my son –

HAMLET   (*aside*) A little more than kin, and less
          than kind.

KING   – how is it that the clouds still hang upon you?

QUEEN	Good Hamlet, cast thy nighted colour off. Do not for ever seek for thy noble father in the dust. Thou know'st 'tis common: all that lives must die.
HAMLET	Ay, madam, it is common.
QUEEN	If it be, why seems it so particular with thee?
HAMLET	Seems, madam? Nay, it is. I know not 'seems'.
KING	'Tis sweet and commendable in your nature, Hamlet, to give these mourning duties to your father, but you must know your father lost a father, that father lost, lost his. We pray you, throw to earth this unprevailing woe . . .

Hamlet stares at him. The king sighs, and, with his queen, leaves the chamber, followed by the court.

HAMLET	Frailty, thy name is woman!

Enter Horatio, Barnardo and Marcellus. Hamlet smiles.

HAMLET	Horatio, or I do forget myself! But what is your affair in Elsinore?

HORATIO   My lord, I came to see your father's funeral.

HAMLET   I prithee, do not mock me, fellow-student. I think it was to see my mother's wedding.

HORATIO   Indeed, my lord, it followed hard upon.

HAMLET   Thrift, thrift, Horatio. The funeral baked meats did coldly furnish forth the marriage tables! (*He sighs and gazes into the distance.*) My father – methinks I see my father –

HORATIO   Where, my lord?

HAMLET   In my mind's eye, Horatio.

HORATIO   My lord, I think I saw him yesternight.

HAMLET   Saw? Who? For God's love let me hear!

HORATIO   Two nights together had these gentlemen on their watch been thus encountered. A figure like your father, armed at point exactly, appears before them, and with solemn march goes slow and stately by them. Thrice he walked. I knew your father, these hands are not more like.

HAMLET   But where was this?

MARCELLUS	My lord, upon the platform where we watched.
HAMLET	Stayed it long?
HORATIO	While one with moderate haste might tell a hundred.
MARCELLUS AND BARNARDO	(*shaking their heads*) Longer, longer!
HORATIO	Not when I saw it.
HAMLET	I will watch tonight, perchance 'twill walk again. Fare you well. (*Horatio and his companions withdraw.*) My father's spirit, in arms! All is not well!

A room in the castle. Laertes, prepared for France, is bidding farewell to Ophelia, his sister.

LAERTES	My necessaries are embarked, farewell. And sister, do not sleep but let me hear from you.
OPHELIA	Do you doubt that?
LAERTES	For Hamlet, and the trifling of his favour, hold it a fashion, and a toy in the blood, no more.

OPHELIA   No more but so?

LAERTES   Fear it, Ophelia, fear it, my dear sister, and
            keep you in the rear of his affection . . . But
            here my father comes!

            Enter Polonius, full of bustle and importance.

POLONIUS   Yet here, Laertes? Aboard, aboard for shame!
            The wind sits in the shoulder of your sail,
            and you are stayed for! There, my blessing
            with thee!

LAERTES   Farewell, Ophelia, and remember well what I
            have said to you.

OPHELIA   'Tis in my memory locked.

LAERTES   Farewell. (*He embraces her, and departs.*)

POLONIUS   What is't, Ophelia, he hath said to you?

OPHELIA   So please you, something touching the
            Lord Hamlet.

POLONIUS   What is't between you? Give me up the truth.

OPHELIA   He hath, my lord, of late made many tenders
            of his affections to me.

POLONIUS   Affection? Pooh, you speak like a green girl!

OPHELIA   My lord, he hath importuned me with love in
             honourable fashion.

POLONIUS   Go to, go to! From this time be somewhat
             scanter of your maiden presence. I would not,
             in plain terms, from this time forth, have you
             so slander any moment leisure as to give
             words or talk with the Lord Hamlet. Look to
             it, I charge you!

OPHELIA   I shall obey you.

             *Night on the battlements. Hamlet, Horatio and
             Marcellus stand together.*

HAMLET   What hour now?

HORATIO   I think it lacks of twelve.

MARCELLUS   No, it is struck.

HORATIO   Indeed, I heard it not. It then draws near the
             season wherein the spirit held his wont to
             walk. (*They stare into the dark.*) Look, my lord,
             it comes!

             The ghost appears, and stalks towards Hamlet.

HAMLET   Angels and ministers of grace defend us! (*The ghost beckons.*) I will follow it!

HORATIO   Do not, my lord!

HAMLET   Why, what should be the fear? I do not set my life at a pin's fee, and for my soul, what can it do to that, being a thing immortal as itself. I'll follow it!

MARCELLUS You shall not, my lord!

HORATIO   Be ruled: you shall not go!

They try to restrain Hamlet. He frees himself and draws his sword.

HAMLET   By heaven, I'll make a ghost of him that lets me! I say away!

The ghost, ever beckoning to Hamlet, mounts steps towards a high, lonely platform.
Hamlet follows.

HAMLET   Go on, I'll follow thee!

The platform is reached. Hamlet's companions have been left behind. Hamlet is alone with the ghost.

255

GHOST   I am thy father's spirit, doomed for a certain
              time to walk the night, and for the day
              confined to fast in fires, till the foul crimes
              done in my days of nature are burnt and
              purged away. (*Hamlet buries his face in his
              hands in horror.*) List, list, O list! If thou didst
              ever thy dear father love –

HAMLET   O God!

GHOST   Revenge his foul and most unnatural murder!

HAMLET   Murder!

GHOST   Murder most foul, as in the best it is. Now,
              Hamlet, hear. 'Tis given out that, sleeping in
              my orchard, a serpent stung me. But know
              thou, noble youth, the serpent that did sting
              thy father's life now wears his crown.

HAMLET   O my prophetic soul! My uncle!

GHOST   Ay, that incestuous, that adulterous beast,
              with witchcraft of his wit, with traitorous
              gifts, won to his shameful lust, the will of my
              most seeming virtuous queen. O Hamlet,
              what a falling-off was there! Let not the royal
              bed of Denmark be a couch for luxury and
              damned incest! But howsoever thou pursuest
              this act, taint not thy mind nor let thy soul

contrive against thy mother aught. Leave her to Heaven . . . Fare thee well . . . Adieu, adieu, adieu. Remember me.

Little by little, the ghost fades into nothingness. Hamlet is left alone, weeping with grief, pity and rage.

HAMLET Remember thee? Ay, thou poor ghost, whiles memory holds a seat in this distracted globe! (*He rushes to the edge of the platform and glares down towards the dark bulk of the castle, from which lights and faint sounds of revelry rise up.*) O most pernicious woman! O villain, villain, smiling damned villain! My tables! (*He drags out his student's commonplace book and begins to write in it feverishly.*) Meet it is I set it down that one may smile and smile and be a villain – so, uncle, there you are! Now to my word. It is, 'Adieu, adieu, remember me!' I have sworn it!

Voices call him from below: My lord, my lord! Lord Hamlet!

Hamlet descends from the platform, and greets his anxious, fearful companions.

MARCELLUS How is't, my noble lord?

HORATIO   What news, Hamlet?

HAMLET   It is an honest ghost, that let me tell you. For your desire to know what is between us, o'ermaster it as you may. And now good friends, as you are friends, scholars and soldiers, give me one poor request.

HORATIO   What is't, my lord?

HAMLET   Never make known what you have seen tonight.

MARCELLUS
AND HORATIO   My lord we will not.

HAMLET   Swear on my sword. (*He holds out his sword. Marcellus and Horatio lay their hands on it and swear. Hamlet now thrusts his sword at them again.*) Here as before, never, so help you mercy, how strange or odd so'er I bear myself, as I perchance hereafter shall think meet to put an antic disposition on, (*He falls into an attitude suggesting madness.*) to note that you know aught of me. Swear.

Much mystified, his companions swear again. Hamlet puts away his sword, and smiles at his friends.

HAMLET   Let us go in together. The time is out of
          joint, O cursed spite, that ever I was born to
          set it right.

          *Hamlet skips ahead of his friends, turns, and adopts
          his attitude of pretended madness. Then he lays a
          warning finger to his lips, and shakes his head.*

          *Polonius's apartment in the castle. Polonius is
          seated at a table. Suddenly his daughter, Ophelia,
          comes rushing in. It is clear that she is upset.*

OPHELIA   O my lord, my lord, I have been so affrighted!

POLONIUS With what, i' the name of God?

OPHELIA   My lord, as I was sewing in my closet, Lord
          Hamlet, with his doublet all unbraced, pale as
          his shirt, his knees knocking each other, and
          with a look so piteous in purport as if he had
          been loosed out of hell to speak of horrors, he
          comes before me!

POLONIUS Mad for thy love?

OPHELIA   My lord, I do not know, but truly I do fear it.

POLONIUS (*rising and taking Ophelia firmly by the hand*)
          Come, go with me. I will go seek the king.
          This is the very ecstasy of love. (*He looks at*

her closely.) Have you given him any hard words of late?

OPHELIA   No, my good lord, but as you did command, I did repel his letters and denied his access to me.

POLONIUS   That hath made him mad. Come, go we to the king.

In the royal apartment, the king and queen are seated, with courtiers in attendance. Polonius and Ophelia appear in the door. Then Polonius, examining the distraught looks of his daughter, decides she is unfit to be brought into the presence of the king. He sends her away and enters on his own.

POLONIUS   (*triumphantly*) I have found the very cause of Hamlet's lunacy!

KING   O speak of that: that do I long to hear!

QUEEN   I doubt it is no other but the main: his father's death and our o'er- hasty marriage.

POLONIUS   (*wisely shaking his head*) I will be brief. Your noble son is mad: mad call I it, for to define true madness, what is't but to be nothing else but mad? But let that go.

QUEEN   (*impatiently*) More matter with less art.

260

POLONIUS   Madam, I swear I use no art at all. That he's
             mad 'tis true, 'tis true 'tis pity, and pity 'tis 'tis
             true – a foolish figure, but farewell it, for I
             will use no art. Perpend. I have a daughter –
             have while she is mine – who in her duty and
             obedience, mark, hath given me this. (*He
             produces a letter which he reads.*) 'To the
             celestial, and my soul's idol, the most
             beautified Ophelia' – That's an ill phrase, a
             vile phrase, 'beautified' is a vile phrase. But
             you shall hear: 'O dear Ophelia, I am ill. I
             have not art to reckon my groans; but that I
             love thee best, O most best, believe it . . .'

QUEEN   Came this from Hamlet to her?

             *Polonius nods and gives the queen the letter. She
             studies it and passes it to the king.*

KING   Do you think 'tis this?

QUEEN   It may be; very like.

KING   How may we try it further?

POLONIUS   You know he walks sometimes four hours
             together here in the lobby? At such a time I'll
             loose my daughter to him. You and I, behind
             an arras there, mark the encounter.

KING   We will try it.

*Hamlet enters, his dress much disordered. He is
reading a book.*

QUEEN   But look where sadly the poor wretch comes.

POLONIUS   Away, I do beseech you both. I'll board
him presently.

*The king and queen, together with the courtiers,
depart, leaving Polonius to confront Hamlet.*

POLONIUS   How does my good lord Hamlet?

HAMLET   Well, God a-mercy.

POLONIUS   Do you know me, my lord?

HAMLET   Excellent well. You are a fishmonger.

POLONIUS   Not I, my lord.

HAMLET   Then I would you were so honest a man.

POLONIUS   Honest, my lord?

HAMLET   Ay, sir, to be honest, as this world goes, is to
be one man picked out of ten thousand.

POLONIUS   That's very true, my lord. (*Aside*) Though this be madness, yet there's method in't.

HAMLET   Have you a daughter?

POLONIUS   I have, my lord.

HAMLET   Let her not walk in the sun. Conception is a blessing, but as your daughter may conceive, friend, look to it.

POLONIUS   (*aside*) Still harping on my daughter. Yet he knew me not at first, he said I was a fishmonger. He is far gone. I'll speak to him again. Will you walk out of the air, my lord?

HAMLET   Into my grave.

POLONIUS   Indeed, that's out of the air. (*Aside*) How pregnant sometimes his replies are! (*To Hamlet*) My lord, I will take my leave of you.

HAMLET   You cannot, sir, take from me anything that I will more willingly part withal – except my life, except my life, except my life. (*Polonius bows and withdraws. Hamlet stares contemptuously after him.*) These tedious old fools!

He goes to a window and gazes out. Far below a cart toils up the hill towards the castle. It bears a huge banner on which is written: 'The best actors in the world, either for Comedy, Tragedy, History . . .' In the cart sit the actors themselves, a perfect painted court, not unlike the royal court of Denmark. Hamlet turns away.

HAMLET (*thoughtfully*) I have heard that guilty creatures sitting at a play, have, by the very cunning of the scene, been struck so to the soul that presently they have proclaimed their malefactions! I will have these players play something like the murder of my father before mine uncle. I'll observe his looks. The spirit that I have seen may be a devil – and the devil hath power t'assume a pleasing shape. I'll have grounds more relative than this. The play's the thing wherein I'll catch the conscience of the king!

A lobby in the castle. The king and Polonius together.

They hide in an alcove behind a curtain. Enter Hamlet, reading. He looks up, deeply troubled.

HAMLET To be, or not to be, that is the question: whether 'tis nobler in the mind to suffer the slings and arrows of outrageous fortune, or to take arms against a sea of troubles, and by opposing, end them. To die, to sleep – no more; and by a sleep to say we end the heartache and the thousand natural shocks that flesh is heir to; 'tis a consummation devoutly to be wished. To die, to sleep – to sleep, perchance to dream – ay, there's the rub, for in that sleep of death what dreams may come, when we have shuffled off this mortal coil, must give us pause . . .

Ophelia approaches.

OPHELIA   Good my lord, how does your honour for this many a day?

HAMLET   I humbly thank you, well, well, well.

OPHELIA   My lord, I have remembrances of yours that I have longed to redeliver. (*She approaches and holds out a bundle of ribbon-tied letters and a necklace.*) Rich gifts wax poor when givers prove unkind. There, my lord.

HAMLET   (*taking the offerings*) I did love you once.

OPHELIA   Indeed, my lord, you made me believe so.

HAMLET   You should not have believed me. I loved you not.

OPHELIA   I was the more deceived.

HAMLET   Get thee to a nunnery. Why, would'st thou be
               a breeder of sinners? Go thy ways to a
               nunnery! Where's your father?

OPHELIA   At home, my lord.

HAMLET   Let the doors be shut upon him, that he may
               play the fool nowhere but in's own house. To
               a nunnery go, and quickly too! Or if thou wilt
               needs marry, marry a fool. For wise men
               know well enough what monsters you make
               of them.

OPHELIA   Heavenly powers restore him!

HAMLET   I have heard of your paintings well enough.
               God hath given you one face, and you make
               yourselves another. You jig and amble, and
               you lisp, you nickname God's creatures and
               you make your wantonness your ignorance.
               Go to, I'll no more on't, it hath made me
               mad. I say we will have no more marriage.
               Those that are married already (all but one)
               shall live, the rest shall keep as they are. To a
               nunnery, go.

               *Hamlet flings the keepsakes in the air. Ophelia
               sinks to the ground. The king and Polonius
               emerge from concealment.*

266

KING   Love? His affections do not that way tend.
There's something in his soul . . . He shall
with speed to England. Madness in great ones
must not unwatched go.

*The Court are all assembled in a great chamber,
awaiting the performance of the players. A
curtain hides the stage. The king and queen are
sitting side by side. Hamlet sits beside Ophelia,
and closely observes the king. The king beckons
to Hamlet.*

KING   Have you heard the argument? Is there no
offence in't?

HAMLET   No, no, they do but jest – poison in jest. No
offence i'the world!

*The king nods. He signs to the musicians. They
sound a fanfare. The curtain parts and reveals a
painted orchard. The action of the play is carried
on in dumbshow, to the accompaniment of music.
The Player King and Player Queen come on, and
fondly embrace.*

*The Player King lies down to sleep. The Player
Queen draws aside. A murderer enters and
cunningly pours poison in the Player King's
sleeping ear. The Player King jerks in violent
pain; then dies. The Player Queen rushes*

267

*forward and clasps her dead husband with
extravagant grief.*

HAMLET   (*to the queen*) Madam, how like you this play?

QUEEN   The lady doth protest too much, methinks.

*On the stage, the murderer takes the Player
Queen by the arm, and offers her jewels. At
first she resists, but then, little by little, she
capitulates. The Player Queen and the murderer
embrace passionately.*

*The king rises from his seat. He is enraged and
terrified by the image of his own crime. The court
rises in consternation.*

HAMLET   What, frighted with false fire?

KING   Give me some light! Away!

*He rushes away, followed by the distracted queen
and all the court. Hamlet and Horatio are
left alone.*

HAMLET   O good Horatio, I'll take the ghost's word for
                  a thousand pound. Didst perceive?

HORATIO   Very well, my lord!

268

Polonius returns, much agitated.

POLONIUS   My lord, the queen would speak with you.

HAMLET   I will come to my mother by and by.
            (*Aside*) I will speak daggers to her but
            use none.

            *In the queen's bedchamber. Polonius attempts to
            give counsel to the queen.*

POLONIUS   Look you lay home to him, tell him his
            pranks have been too broad to bear with. Pray
            you be round!

QUEEN   Fear me not. Withdraw, I hear him coming!

            *Hastily, Polonius conceals himself behind a
            curtain. Hamlet enters, wild of aspect.*

HAMLET   How now, mother, what's the matter?

QUEEN   Hamlet, thou hast thy father much offended.

HAMLET   Mother, you have my father much offended.

QUEEN   Come, come, you answer with an idle tongue.

HAMLET   Go, go, you question with a wicked tongue.

He stares at her menacingly. She retreats. He seizes her and forces her to sit on the bed.

HAMLET   Come, come, you shall not budge –

QUEEN   What wilt thou do? Thou wilt not murder me? Help, ho!

POLONIUS   (*behind the curtain*) What ho! Help!

HAMLET   (*rushing to the curtain*) How now? A rat! Dead for a ducat, dead! (*He thrusts his sword through the curtain. There is a cry, and the sound of a body falling. Hamlet draws out his bloody sword. He looks to the queen.*) Is it the King? (*He draws aside the curtain, and sees Polonius, dead.*)

QUEEN   O what a rash and bloody deed is this!

HAMLET   (*to the dead Polonius*) Thou wretched, rash, intruding fool, farewell; I took thee for thy better. Thou find'st to be too busy is some danger. (*To the queen*) Leave wringing your hands. Peace, sit you down, and let me wring your heart. (*They sit, side by side, on the bed. Hamlet holds up a locket he wears round his neck and shows it to his mother.*) Look here upon this picture, (*He drags a locket from his mother's neck and compares it with the other.*) and on this, the counterfeit presentment of two

270

brothers. Have you eyes? Could you on this
fair mountain feed and batten on this moor?
Ha, have you eyes? You cannot call it love, for
at your age the heyday in the blood is tame,
it's humble and waits upon the judgement,
and what judgement would step from this
to this?

QUEEN   O speak to me no more. These words like
daggers enter in my ear!

HAMLET   A murderer and a villain –

QUEEN   No more!

HAMLET   A king of shreds and patches –

*Suddenly, the ghost appears. Hamlet stares at
it, wild-eyed.*

QUEEN   Alas, he's mad!

HAMLET   (*to ghost*) Do you not come your tardy son
to chide?

GHOST   Do not forget. This visitation is to whet thy
almost blunted purpose. But look, amazement
on thy mother sits. Speak to her, Hamlet.

HAMLET   How is't with you, lady?

QUEEN   Alas, how is't with you? Whereon do you look?

HAMLET   On him, on him! Look you how pale he
             glares! Do you see nothing there?

QUEEN   Nothing at all –

HAMLET   Nor did you nothing hear?

QUEEN   No, nothing but ourselves!

             The ghost begins to depart . . .

HAMLET   Why, look you there, look how it steals away,
             my father in his habit as he lived! Look where
             he goes!

QUEEN   This is the very coinage of your brain . . .

             *Hamlet shakes his head. He rises and goes to the
             dead Polonius.*

HAMLET   This man shall send me packing. I'll lug the
             guts into the neighbour room. This counsellor
             is now most still, most secret, and most grave,
             who was in life a foolish prating knave. (*He
             seizes hold of the dead man's feet and begins to
             drag him to the door.*) Come, sir, draw toward
             an end with you. Good night, mother.

Hamlet departs with the body. The king enters, followed by his attendants.

KING   How does Hamlet?

QUEEN   Mad as the sea and wind. In his lawless fit, behind the arras hearing something stir, whips out his rapier, cries 'A rat, a rat!' and kills the unseen good old man!

KING   O heavy deed! Where is he gone?

QUEEN   To draw apart the body –

KING   *(to attendants)* Go seek him out!

The body of Polonius has not been found; but Hamlet has been seized and brought before the king.

KING   Now, Hamlet, where's Polonius?

HAMLET   At supper.

KING   At supper? Where?

HAMLET   Not where he eats, but where he's eaten; a certain convocation of politic worms are e'en at him.

KING   Where is Polonius?

HAMLET   In heaven, send thither to see; if your
                messenger find him not there, seek him i' the
                other place yourself. But if indeed you find
                him not within this month, you shall nose
                him as you go up the stairs into the lobby.

KING   (*to attendants*) Go seek him there. (*To Hamlet*)
                Hamlet, this deed must send thee hence.
                Therefore prepare thyself for England.
                (*Hamlet shrugs his shoulders and departs. The
                king looks after him savagely.*) England, if my
                love thou holds at aught, thou mayst not
                coldly set our sovereign process, which
                imports at full, by letters congruing to that
                effect, the present death of Hamlet! Do it,
                England, for like the hectic in my blood he
                rages, and thou must cure me!

                *In the royal apartment, the king and queen look
                to one another in dismay as a strange, distracted
                wailing is heard. Ophelia enters, all in ragged
                white, crying and laughing and singing. Wild
                flowers are in her hair, and she carries a posy. The
                death of her father and the loss of Hamlet have
                driven her mad.*

OPHELIA   (*singing*)
                    He is dead and gone, lady,

                              274

He is dead and gone . . .
(*She drifts away.*)

KING O Gertrude, Gertrude, when sorrows come,
they come not single spies, but in
battalions . . .

There is a violent commotion outside. A
soldier enters.

SOLDIER Save yourself, my lord! Young Laertes in
riotous head o'erbears your officers! The
rabble call him lord!

Laertes with armed followers, bursts in.

LAERTES (*to followers*) Sirs, stand you all without! O
thou vile king, give me my father!

QUEEN Calmly, good Laertes. (*She tries to restrain him.*)

KING Let him go, Gertrude, do not fear our person.
There's such divinity doth hedge a king that
treason can but peep at what it would. Tell
me, Laertes, why thou art thus incensed?

LAERTES Where is my father?

KING Dead.

275

QUEEN   But not by him!

KING   I am guiltless of thy father's death, and am –

             He breaks off as a sound of strange singing
             is heard.

LAERTES   What noise is that?

             Ophelia returns, in her distracted state. Laertes
             stares at her in horror.

OPHELIA   They bore him bare-faced on the bier
                And on his grave rained many a tear –

             She stops, and, plucking flowers from her posy,
             presents them to Laertes.

OPHELIA   There's rosemary, that's for remembrance.
             (*To the queen*) There's fennel for you, and
             columbines. (*To the king*) There's rue for you.
             And here's some for me. We may call it herb
             o' grace on Sundays. You must wear your rue
             with a difference. I would give you some
             violets, but they withered all when my father
             died. They say he made a good end.

             All watch her, filled with pity. Laertes weeps for
             his sister.

OPHELIA   (*singing*)
               And will he not come again,
               And will he not come again?
               No, no, he's dead,
               Go to thy deathbed,
               He never will come again.

She drifts out of the apartment, out of the castle and into the woods beyond, until she comes to a stream, and there, still singing, clambers onto the branch of a willow, which breaks and casts her into the brook. 'Her clothes spread wide, and mermaid-like awhile they bore her up. But long it could not be till that her garments, heavy with their drink, pulled the poor wretch from her melodious lay to muddy death.'

The ship taking Hamlet to England has been attacked by pirates; and Hamlet, discovering the plot against his life, has boarded the pirate vessel and, in exchange for promises of reward, has been landed safely once more on Danish soil. He and Horatio are together, near to a churchyard. As they approach, they see a gravedigger at work, and singing.

GRAVEDIGGER   In youth when I did love, did love,
               Methought it was very sweet . . .

HAMLET   Hath this fellow no feeling for his business?

277

He sings in grave-making. (*He addresses the gravedigger*) What man dost thou dig for?

GRAVEDIGGER   For no man, sir.

HAMLET   For what woman then?

GRAVEDIGGER   For none neither.

HAMLET   Who is to be buried in it?

GRAVEDIGGER   One that was a woman, sir; but rest her soul, she's dead. (*He picks up a skull from the earth.*) Here's a skull now hath lien you i' the earth three-and-twenty years.

HAMLET   Whose was it?

GRAVEDIGGER   A whoreson mad fellow's it was! This same skull, sir, was Yorick's skull, the King's jester.

Hamlet takes the skull and gazes at it wonderingly.

HAMLET   This?

GRAVEDIGGER   E'en that.

HAMLET   Alas, poor Yorick, I knew him, Horatio, a fellow of infinite jest. (*To the skull*) No one

278

now to mock your own grinning? Now get you to my lady's chamber, and tell her, let her paint an inch thick, to this favour she must come. Let her laugh at that. But soft, here comes the King, the Queen, the courtiers!

A funeral procession approaches. The king, queen, Laertes, and all the court follow a coffin. A priest is in attendance. Hamlet and Horatio withdraw behind a monument, to watch. The procession reaches the grave, and the coffin is lowered in. The priest turns away.

LAERTES   Must there be no more done? (*The priest shakes his head.*) I tell thee, churlish priest, a ministering angel shall my sister be when thou liest howling!

HAMLET   What, the fair Ophelia!

QUEEN   (*scattering flowers on the coffin*) Sweets to the sweet. Farewell.

LAERTES   Hold off the earth awhile, till I have caught her once more in mine arms!

He leaps down into the grave. Hamlet rushes upon the scene.

HAMLET   What is he whose grief bears such an emphasis?

279

LAERTES	(*looking up*) The devil take thy soul!
	Hamlet leaps down into the grave and grapples with Laertes.
KING	Pluck them asunder!
QUEEN	Hamlet, Hamlet!
HAMLET	I loved Ophelia! Forty thousand brothers could not with all their quantity of love make up my sum!
KING	O he is mad, Laertes!
QUEEN	For love of God, forbear him!
	Courtiers drag the warring youths apart. They glare at each other. Then Hamlet shrugs his shoulders.
HAMLET	Hear you, sir, what is the reason you use me thus? I loved you ever – but it is no matter. Let Hercules himself do what he may, the cat will mew, and dog will have his day.
	An apartment in the castle. The king and Laertes are together.
KING	Hamlet comes back; what would you

undertake in deed to show yourself your
father's son?

LAERTES   To cut his throat i' the church.

KING   (*nodding*) Will you be ruled by me?

LAERTES   Ay, my lord.

KING   You have been talked of since your travel
much, and that in Hamlet's hearing, for a
quality wherein they say you shine.

LAERTES   What part is that?

KING   For art and exercise in your defence, and for
your rapier most especial. This report did
Hamlet so envenom with his envy that he
could do nothing but wish and beg your
sudden coming o'er to play with you.

LAERTES   What out of this, my lord?

KING   Bring you in fine together, and wager on your
heads. He being remiss, and free from all
contriving, will not peruse the foils, so that
with ease, or with a little shuffling, you may
choose a sword unbated, and in a pass of
practice requite him for your father!

LAERTES   (*eagerly*) I will do't, and for that purpose I'll
           anoint my sword. I bought an unction from a
           mountebank, so mortal that but to dip a knife
           in it . . . (*He makes an expressive gesture,
           indicating sudden death.*)

KING   Let's think further of this. When in your
           motion you are hot and dry, as make your
           bouts more violent to that end, and that he
           calls for drink, I'll have prepared him a
           chalice for the nonce, whereon but sipping, if
           he by chance escape your venomed stuck, our
           purpose may hold there.

           They gaze into one another's eyes, deeply.

           *The great hall of the castle. Hamlet and Horatio
           are together. The fencing match with Laertes has
           been agreed to. A courtier enters.*

COURTIER   My lord, his majesty sends to know if your
           pleasure hold to play with Laertes.

HAMLET   I am constant to my purpose. (*The courtier
           bows and departs.*)

HORATIO   You will lose, my lord.

HAMLET   I do not think so. But thou would'st not think
           how ill all's here about my heart – but no matter.

282

HORATIO   If your mind dislike anything, obey it. I will
            forestall their repair hither and say you are
            not fit.

HAMLET   We defy augury. There is special providence
            in the fall of a sparrow. The readiness is all.
            Let be.

            *Trumpets sound, heralding the approach of the
            king and queen, and all the court, to witness the
            fencing match. They seat themselves. Foils are
            brought forward. They are offered first to Laertes.
            He chooses one, and flourishes it.*

LAERTES   This is too heavy. Let me see another.

            *He takes another, which suits him better. He
            exchanges a secret nod with the king while
            Hamlet chooses a sword for himself.*

HAMLET   This likes me well.

            *A servant brings a goblet of wine and sets it
            beside the king.*

KING   Come, begin. And you, the judges, bear a
            wary eye.

            The adversaries' swords are put together.

HAMLET   Come on, sir!

                They fence. Hamlet scores a hit.

JUDGE   A hit, a very palpable hit!

                *The duellists part. The king frowns. He drops
                something in the goblet.*

KING   Hamlet, this pearl is thine! Give him the cup!

HAMLET   I'll play this bout first. Set it by awhile.
                Come. (*They fence again. Again Hamlet scores a
                hit.*) Another hit, what say you?

LAERTES   I do confess't.

KING   (*to the queen*) Our son shall win.

QUEEN   Here, Hamlet, take my napkin, rub thy brows.
                (*She takes up the goblet.*) The Queen carouses
                to thy fortune, Hamlet!

KING   Gertrude, do not drink!

QUEEN   I will, my lord, I pray you pardon me.
                (*She drinks.*)

KING   (*aside*) It is the poisoned cup! It is too late.

QUEEN   (*to Hamlet*) Come, let me wipe your face.

Hamlet goes to his mother, Laertes lunges at him and wounds his arm. Hamlet turns, incensed. They begin to fence again, but with a deadly fury. Suddenly Laertes is disarmed. Hamlet takes up the fallen sword, stares at its unbated tip. He throws his own sword to Laertes, and with the poisoned weapon begins to fight again. Laertes is wounded.

SERVANT   Look to the Queen!

The fighting stops. The queen has fallen back. She is dying.

KING   She swoons to see them bleed!

QUEEN   No, no, the drink, the drink! O my dear Hamlet! The drink, the drink! I am poisoned! (*She dies.*)

HAMLET   O villainy! Let the door be locked! Treachery, seek it out!

He rushes at the king. The court seeks to fly from the scene. Laertes has fallen. His wound is bleeding.

LAERTES   It is here, Hamlet. Hamlet, thou art slain, no medicine in the world can do thee good, in thee there is not half an hour of life. The treacherous instrument is in thine hand, unbated and envenomed. The foul practice hath turned itself on me. The King – the King's to blame!

Hamlet seizes the king and stabs him with the poisoned blade.

HAMLET Venom, do thy work! (*He takes hold of the poisoned goblet and forces its contents down the king's throat.*) Here, thou incestuous, murderous, damned Dane, drink off this potion! Follow my mother! (*The king dies.*)

LAERTES Exchange forgiveness with me, noble Hamlet.

Hamlet takes his offered hand. Then Laertes, doomed like all who had touched the corruption of the state, dies.

HAMLET Heaven make thee free of it. I follow thee. (*He staggers. Horatio comes to support him.*) I am dead, Horatio. (*He tries to embrace the dead queen.*) Wretched Queen, adieu. (*He almost falls, and Horatio eases him into the chair from which the king has fallen.*) This fell sergeant, Death, is strict in his arrest. If thou didst ever hold me in thy heart, absent thee from felicity

awhile, and in this harsh world draw thy
breath in pain to tell my story . . . (*He tries to smile.*) The rest is silence . . . (*He dies.*)

HORATIO   Now cracks a noble heart. Good night, sweet prince, and flights of angels sing thee to thy rest.

The curtain falls . . .

The Winter's Tale

To my mind, of all Shakespeare's plays, *The Winter's Tale* is the most moving and the most magical. It is the story of King Leontes of Sicily, who, in a fit of mad jealousy, brings about the death of his beloved little son and his gracious queen, and causes his baby daughter to be carried away to some wild and savage place, and there left to the mercy of the elements. It is the story of that little daughter and what becomes of her; and of the old shepherd who finds her and brings her up as his own, not knowing she is a princess until . . .

The first part of the play is all terror and darkness; the second, all laughter and light. 'Thou met'st with things dying,' says the old shepherd to his son who has come to tell him of a man being eaten by a bear; 'and I with things new-born,' he says, and shows him the babe.

288

The Characters in the Play

in order of appearance

LEONTES	*King of Sicilia*
MAMILLIUS	*young Prince of Sicilia*
CAMILLO	*a Lord of Sicilia*
POLIXENES	*King of Bohemia*
HERMIONE	*Queen to Leontes*
ANTIGONUS	*a Lord of Sicilia*
SERVANT	*to Leontes*
PAULINA	*wife to Antigonus*
A LORD	
A JUDGE	
AN OLD SHEPHERD	
THE OLD SHEPHERD'S SON	
TIME	
AUTOLYCUS	*a rogue*
PERDITA	*daughter to Leontes and Hermione*
FLORIZEL	*Prince of Bohemia, son of Polixenes*
FOUR GENTLEMEN	
	Other ladies and gentlemen, servants, shepherds and shepherdesses

On a terrible day, a sudden madness strikes down Leontes, the king of Sicilia. In the twinkling of an eye, it turns him against those he loves best: Hermione, his queen, and Polixenes, king of Bohemia, his childhood friend and guest. He becomes convinced they are lovers and Polixenes the father of Hermione's unborn child.

The curtain rises on the palace of Leontes. It is winter. Polixenes and Hermione walk together. Leontes watches from a little distance, his arm about the shoulders of Mamillius, his little son.

LEONTES   Too hot, too hot! To mingle friendship far
        is mingling bloods. I have tremor cordis on
        me; my heart dances, but not for joy – not
        joy. Go play, boy, play. Thy mother plays,
        and I play too, but so disgrac'd a part.
        How now, boy? What! Hast smutched thy
        nose? They say it is a copy out of mine.
        Come, captain, we must be neat. (*He wipes
        his nose.*)

MAMILLIUS   I am like you, they say.

LEONTES   Why, that's some comfort. Go play,
        Mamillius.

        Mamillius leaves.

LEONTES   What! Camillo there?

CAMILLO   Ay, my good lord.

LEONTES   Ha' not you seen, Camillo – but that's past
                 doubt – that my wife is slippery?

CAMILLO   You never spoke what did become you less
                 than this!

LEONTES   Is whispering nothing? Is leaning cheek
                 to cheek? Kissing with inside lip? Is
                 this nothing?

CAMILLO   Good my lord, be cur'd of this diseas'd
                 opinion, and betimes, for 'tis most
                 dangerous.

LEONTES   Say it be, 'tis true.

CAMILLO   No, no, my lord!

LEONTES   It is: you lie. Might'st bespice a cup to give
                 mine enemy a lasting wink?

                 Leontes departs.

CAMILLO   What case stand I in? I must be the
                 poisoner of good Polixenes.

                 Polixenes enters.

POLIXENES	The king hath on him such a countenance as he had lost some province. What is breeding that changes thus his manners?
CAMILLO	Sir, I will tell you – I am appointed him to murder you.
POLIXENES	By whom, Camillo?
CAMILLO	By the king.
POLIXENES	For what?
CAMILLO	He thinks, nay, with all confidence he swears, that you have touch'd his queen forbiddenly.
POLIXENES	O then, my best blood turn to an infected jelly! How should this grow?
CAMILLO	I know not; but I am sure 'tis safer to avoid what's grown than question how 'tis born. For myself, I'll put my fortunes to your service, which are here by this discovery lost.
POLIXENES	I do believe thee: I saw his heart in's face. Give me thy hand. My ships are ready.

In the queen's apartment, Hermione is with

292

her ladies who are playing with little Mamillius.

HERMIONE   Come, sir, pray you sit by us, and tell's a tale.

MAMILLIUS   Merry, or sad, shall't be?

HERMIONE   As merry as you will.

MAMILLIUS   A sad tale's best for winter. I have one of sprites and goblins.

HERMIONE   Sit down, and do your best to fright me with your sprites.

MAMILLIUS   There was a man – dwelt by a churchyard . . .

Leontes and lords enter.

LEONTES   Bear the boy hence, he shall not come about her.

HERMIONE   What is this? Sport?

LEONTES   Away with him! And let her sport herself with that she's big with, for 'tis Polixenes has made thee swell thus. She's an adultress! (*The child is removed.*)

293

HERMIONE	Should a villain say so, the most replenish'd villain in the world, he were as much more villain: you, my lord, do but mistake.
LEONTES	You have mistook, my lady, Polixenes for Leontes. Away with her, to prison!
HERMIONE	Adieu, my lord, I never wish'd to see you sorry; now I trust I shall.

The queen departs under guard. Her ladies are in tears but she does not cry and gestures to them to be brave as she passes. Antigonus, an old nobleman, speaks up for her.

ANTIGONUS	I dare my life lay down that the queen is spotless.
LEONTES	Cease, no more. You smell this business with a sense as cold as is a dead man's nose; but I do see't and feel't. I have dispatch'd to sacred Delphos, to Apollo's temple. Though I am satisfied, yet shall the Oracle give rest to th'minds of others – such as he. (*He points to Antigonus.*)

Mamillius has fallen sick and a servant brings news of the child's condition to Leontes.

294

LEONTES   How does the boy?

SERVANT   He took good rest tonight; 'tis hop'd his sickness is discharg'd.

LEONTES   Go, see how he fares.

Hermione, in prison, has given birth to an infant girl. Her good friend, Paulina, wife of Antigonus, decides to take the baby to Leontes in the hope of curing him of his madness. But when she attempts to gain audience with Leontes, he is outraged.

LEONTES   Away with that audacious lady! Antigonus, I charg'd thee that she should not come about me. Canst not rule her?

ANTIGONUS   Hang all the husbands that cannot do that feat, you'll leave yourself hardly one subject.

PAULINA   Good my liege, I come from your good queen.

LEONTES   Good queen?

PAULINA   The good queen – for she is good – hath brought you forth a daughter, here 'tis.

LEONTES	A mankind witch! Hence with her, out o' door! Give her the bastard, thou dotard! Tak't up, I say: give it to thy crone!

Antigonus stands frozen.

LEONTES	He dreads his wife. This brat is none of mine.
PAULINA	It is yours: and so like you, 'tis the worse.
LEONTES	I'll have thee burnt!
PAULINA	I care not.
LEONTES	Out of the chamber with her!
PAULINA	I'll be gone. Look to your babe, my lord, 'tis yours.

She departs, leaving the child to its father's mercy.

LEONTES	Thou, traitor, hast set on thy wife to this. My child? Away with't! Go, take it to the fire.
LORD	Beseech your highness, on our knees we beg that you do change this purpose, which, being so horrible, so bloody, must lead on to some foul issue.

They kneel.

LEONTES   Be it: let it live. What will you adventure to save this brat's life?

ANTIGONUS   Any thing, my lord.

LEONTES   Mark, and perform it. We enjoin thee that thou carry this female bastard hence, and that thou bear it to some remote and desert place, quite out of our dominions; and that there thou leave it to its own protection: take it up.

ANTIGONUS   Come on, poor babe: some powerful spirit instruct the kites and ravens to be thy nurses.

Antigonus takes up the babe and hastens away.

SERVANT   Please your highness, posts from those you sent to the Oracle are come.

LEONTES   Prepare you, my lords, summon a session that we may arraign our most disloyal lady.

In the place of justice, Hermione stands before her accuser.

JUDGE	Hermione, queen to the worthy Leontes, king of Sicilia, thou art here accused and arraigned of high treason, in committing adultery with Polixenes, king of Bohemia.
HERMIONE	You, my lord, best know my past life hath been as continent, as chaste, as true, as I am now unhappy. Your honours, I do refer me to the Oracle: Apollo be my judge!
LORD	This your request is altogether just.

The officers go to fetch the messengers.

HERMIONE	The Emperor of Russia was my father. O that he were alive, and here beholding his daughter's trial! That he did but see the flatness of my misery, yet with eyes of pity, not revenge.

The officers return with the two messengers.

LEONTES	Break up the seals and read.
JUDGE	(*reading*) Hermione is chaste; Polixenes blameless; Camillo a true subject; Leontes a jealous tyrant; his innocent babe truly begotten; and the king shall live without an heir, if that which is lost be not found.

298

LORDS   Now blessed be the great Apollo.

LEONTES   There is no truth at all in the Oracle!

                    *There is a clap of thunder. A servant
                    rushes in.*

LEONTES   The sessions shall proceed: this is mere
                    falsehood.

SERVANT   My lord the king! Your son is gone!

LEONTES   How? Gone?

SERVANT   Is dead.

                    *Leontes stares in horror at what his madness
                    has brought about.*

LEONTES   Apollo's angry, and the heavens
                    themselves do strike at my injustice!

                    *Hermione swoons. She is carried away by her
                    ladies with Paulina in tearful attendance.*

PAULINA   This news is mortal to the queen. Look
                    down and see what death is doing.

LEONTES   Take her hence. Beseech you, tenderly
                    apply to her some remedies for life.

I'll reconcile me to Polixenes, new
woo my queen, recall the good Camillo.
How his piety does my deeds make
the blacker!

Paulina returns.

PAULINA   The queen! The sweet'st, dear'st creature's
dead! O thou tyrant! Betake thee to
nothing but despair.

LEONTES   Go on, go on: I have deserv'd all tongues
to talk their bitt'rest. Prithee bring me to
the dead bodies of my queen and son; one
grave shall be for both: upon them shall
the causes of their deaths appear, unto our
shame perpetual.

*Antigonus, obeying his master's harsh
command, takes the babe and sets sail from
Sicilia. On board ship, Antigonus has a
strange vision in which Hermione appears
before him. Such is the nature of the
vision that Antigonus is convinced of
Hermione's guilt.*

HERMIONE   Good Antigonus, since fate hath made thy
person for the thrower-out of my poor
babe, places remote enough are in
Bohemia, there weep, and leave it crying;

and, for the babe is counted lost forever,
Perdita, I prithee call it.

*Antigonus, having landed on the rocky sea
coast of Bohemia in the midst of a terrible
storm, leaves the child to its fate.*

ANTIGONUS   Blossom, speed thee well. There lie, and
there thy character.

*He places a box and bundle of possessions
beside the baby.*

ANTIGONUS   Farewell, the day frowns more and more:
thou'rt like to have a lullaby too rough. (*A
bear appears.*) I am gone forever! (*Exit,
pursued by a bear.*)

*The storm increases in fury and overwhelms
the waiting ship. Meanwhile, a shepherd
searching for lost sheep, comes upon the babe.*

SHEPHERD   What have we here? Mercy on's, a barne?
I'll take it up for pity: yet I'll tarry till my
son come. Ahoa!

An answering shout. Enter the shepherd's son.

SON   I have seen two such sights, by sea
and land!

301

SHEPHERD   Why boy, how is it?

In answer to the shepherd's question, the son tells how he saw all the sailors drowned and Antigonus eaten by the bear.

SHEPHERD   Now bless thyself: thou met'st with things dying, I with things new born. Here's a sight for thee: look thee, a bearing-cloth for a squire's child. Look thee here, take up, boy, open it. What's within, boy?

His son opens the box and finds Hermione's jewels.

SON   You're a made old man! Gold! All gold!

SHEPHERD   This is fairy gold, and 'twill prove so. 'Tis a lucky day, boy, and we'll do good deeds on't.

The sky lightens and across the landscape of Bohemia a strange spectre strides: a pale figure bearing an hourglass. It is Time.

TIME   In the name of Time, I slide over sixteen years. In fair Bohemia, a son of the king's which Florizel I now name to you. And Perdita now grown in grace, a shepherd's daughter.

*In the royal palace, Polixenes and Camillo
stand together, gazing out of the window. It is
high summer.*

POLIXENES   Say to me, when sawest thou the Prince
            Florizel, my son?

CAMILLO   Sir, it is three days since I saw the prince.

POLIXENES   I have this intelligence, that he is seldom
            from the house of a most homely
            shepherd: a man, they say, that from
            very nothing, is grown into an
            unspeakable estate.

CAMILLO   I have heard, sir, of such a man, who hath
            a daughter of most rare note.

POLIXENES   Thou shalt accompany us to the place.

CAMILLO   I obey your command.

POLIXENES   My best Camillo! We must disguise
            ourselves.

*On a country road, a lively figure appears. It
is Autolycus, a cheerful pilferer of everything
that has not been nailed down.*

AUTOLYCUS   (*singing*)
                   When daffodils begin to peer,
                   With heigh the doxy over the dale,
                   Why then comes in the sweet o' the
                                                    year.
                   For the red blood reigns in the winter's
                                                    pale.

                   My father named me Autolycus, who was
                   likewise a snapper-up of unconsidered
                   trifles. (*He sees the shepherd's son
                   approaching.*) A prize, a prize!

SON   Let me see, what am I to buy for our
                   sheep-shearing feast? Three pound of
                   sugar, five pound of currants, rice: what
                   will this sister of mine do with rice? But
                   my father hath made her Mistress of
                   the Feast –

                   *Autolycus flings himself in the son's path,
                   wailing and moaning.*

AUTOLYCUS   O help me, help me! I am robbed, sir,
                   and beaten.

SON   Lend me thy hand, I'll help thee.

AUTOLYCUS   O good sir, tenderly, oh!

As the son helps Autolycus to his feet, his pocket is skilfully picked.

SON   How now? Canst stand? Dost lack any money? I have a little money for thee.

AUTOLYCUS   No, good sweet sir! Offer me no money, I pray you; that kills my heart.

SON   Then fare thee well, I must go buy spices for our sheep-shearing.

The son departs.

AUTOLYCUS   (*examining his booty*) Prosper you, sweet sir. I'll be with you at your sheep-shearing too. (*He sets off along the road, singing.*)

> Jog on, jog on, the footpath way,
> And merrily hent the stile-a:
> A merry heart goes all the day.
> Your sad tires in a mile-a.

Before the shepherd's cottage, everything is in readiness for the sheep-shearing. There is music and dancing and Perdita, attired as Queen of the Feast, speaks to Florizel who is dressed as a very grand shepherd.

*She moves away from Florizel and gives
flowers and herbs to Polixenes and Camillo
who are strangers at the feast.*

PERDITA   Reverend sirs, for you, there's rosemary
             and rue; grace and remembrance be
             to you both, and welcome to our
             sheep-shearing.

             Florizel returns to her side.

FLORIZEL   Come, our dance I pray, your hand,
             my Perdita.

             He leads her off and they join the dance.

POLIXENES   This is the prettiest low-born lass, that
             ever ran on greensward.

CAMILLO   Good sooth, she is the queen of curds
             and cream!

POLIXENES   Pray good shepherd, what fair swain is
             this, which dances with your daughter?

SHEPHERD   They call him Doricles. He says he loves
             my daughter: I think so too. I think there
             is not half a kiss to choose who loves
             another best. (*Autolycus enters, singing.*)

AUTOLYCUS

Will you buy any tape,
Or lace for your cape,
My dainty duck, my dear-a?
Any silk, any thread,
Any toys for your head . . .
Of the new'st, and fin'st, wear-a?

*The dancers eagerly stream after him. Perdita
and Florizel are left. Polixenes beckons
them near.*

POLIXENES

Sooth, when I was young, and handed
love, as you do, I was wont to load my she
with knacks; I would have ransack'd the
pedlar's silken treasury –

FLORIZEL

(*with dramatic sincerity*) Old sir, I know she
prizes not such trifles as these are. The
gifts she looks from me, are pack'd and
lock'd up in my heart, which I have given
already, but not delivered.

SHEPHERD

Take hands, a bargain; and friends
unknown, you shall bear witness to't: I
give my daughter to him, and will make
her portion equal his. Come, your hand:
and daughter, yours.

POLIXENES

Soft, swain, awhile, beseech you. Have you
a father?

307

FLORIZEL   I have: but what of him?

POLIXENES   Knows he of this?

FLORIZEL   He neither does, nor shall.

POLIXENES   By my white beard, you offer him a wrong
something unfilial. Let him know't.

FLORIZEL   He shall not: mark our contract.

POLIXENES   (*revealing himself*) Mark your divorce,
young sir, whom son I dare not call: thou
art too base to be acknowledged; thou a
sceptre's heir that thus affects a sheep-
hook! Thou, old traitor, I am sorry, that by
hanging thee, I can but shorten thy life
one week. And thou, if ever henceforth
thou hoop his body more with thy
embraces, I will devise a death, as cruel for
thee as thou art tender to't.

He storms away, leaving all aghast.

PERDITA   I was not much afeared: for once, or twice
I was about to speak, and tell him plainly,
the self-same sun that shines upon his
court hides not his visage from our
cottage, but looks on alike. (*To Florizel*)
Will't please you, sir, be gone?

The Winter's Tale

SHEPHERD

O sir, you have undone a man of fourscore three. (*To Perdita*) O cursed wretch, thou knew'st this was the prince! Undone, undone! If I might die within this hour, I have lived to die when I desire.

The old shepherd leaves.

FLORIZEL

(*to Camillo and Perdita*) Why look you so upon me? I am sorry, not afear'd: delay'd, but nothing alter'd: what I was, I am –

CAMILLO

Gracious my lord –

FLORIZEL

Camillo, not for Bohemia will I break my oath to this fair belov'd. This you may know, and so deliver, I am put to sea with her whom here I cannot hold on shore. I have a vessel rides fast by.

CAMILLO

This is desperate sir. Have you thought on a place whereto you'll go?

FLORIZEL

Not any yet.

CAMILLO

Then list to me. Make for Sicilia and there present yourself and your fair princess 'fore Leontes. (*Autolycus walks by.*) We'll make an instrument of this. How now, good fellow?

309

AUTOLYCUS   I am a poor fellow, sir.

CAMILLO   Why, be so still. Yet for the outside of thy
poverty we must make an exchange:
therefore discase thee instantly and change
garments with this gentleman. There's
some boot. (*Gives him money.*) What I do
next shall be to tell the king of this escape
to force him after.

*The terrified shepherd and his son are on their
way to the palace with the box and bundle
of possessions that they found with the
infant Perdita.*

SON   There is no other way but to tell the king
she's a changeling, and none of your flesh
and blood.

SHEPHERD   I will tell the king all, every word, yea, and
his son's pranks too. There is that in this
fardel will make him scratch his beard. (*He
taps the bundle.*)

Autolycus enters. He has overheard the last.

AUTOLYCUS   How now, rustics, whither are you bound?

SHEPHERD   To the palace, and it like your worship.

AUTOLYCUS   What's in the fardel? Wherefore that box?

SHEPHERD   Sir, there lies such secrets in this fardel
              and box which none must know but
              the king.

AUTOLYCUS   Age, thou hast lost thy labour. The king is
              not at the palace. He is gone aboard a new
              ship. I'll bring you where he is.

SON   He seems to be of great authority. Close
              with him, give him gold.

SHEPHERD   An't please you sir, to undertake the
              business for us, here is that gold I have.

AUTOLYCUS   Walk before, toward the sea-side. (*They
              walk on.*) If I had a mind to be honest, I
              see Fortune would not suffer me: she
              drops booties in my mouth. To the prince
              will I present them, there may be matter
              in it.

              *In Sicilia, Leontes still mourns the loss of his
              Hermione as does Paulina of her Antigonus.
              His lords try to persuade him to take
              another wife.*

LORD   Sir, you have done enough, and have
              perform'd a saint-like sorrow.

PAULINA

You are one of those would have him wed again. There is none worthy, respecting her that's gone. Besides, has not the divine Apollo said that King Leontes shall not have an heir till his lost child be found?

LEONTES

My true Paulina, we shall not marry till thou bid'st us.

PAULINA

That shall be when your first queen's again in breath: never till then. (*As she speaks, a servant enters.*)

SERVANT

One that gives out himself Prince Florizel, son of Polixenes, with his princess – she the fairest I have yet beheld – desires access to your high presence.

LEONTES

He comes not like to his father's greatness. Bring them to our embracement. Still, 'tis strange he thus should steal upon us.

Florizel and Perdita enter.

LEONTES

Were I but twenty-one, your father's image is so hit in you – his very air – that I should call you brother. Welcome hither, as is the spring to th'earth.

A lord enters.

LORD   Please you, great sir, Polixenes greets you
                from himself by me; desires you to attach
                his son, who has fled from his father, from
                his hopes, and with a shepherd's daughter.

LEONTES   Where's Polixenes? Speak.

LORD   Here, in your city. To your court whiles
                he was hastening, meets he on the way
                the father of this seeming lady and
                her brother.

PERDITA   O my poor father!

LEONTES   (to Florizel) You are married?

FLORIZEL   We are not, sir, nor are we like to be.

LEONTES   My lord, is this the daughter of a king?

FLORIZEL   She is, when once she is my wife.

LEONTES   That 'once', I see, by your good father's
                speed, will come on very slowly.

FLORIZEL   Beseech you sir, step forth mine advocate.
                At your request, my father will grant
                precious things as trifles.

LEONTES   I will to your father. Come.

*In Sicilia, church bells are ringing
everywhere. The two kings have met. The old
shepherd's box and bundle which contained
the secrets of Perdita's birth have been opened.
The Oracle has been fulfilled: the king's
daughter has been found.*

*Autolycus and three gentlemen enter. A
fourth approaches.*

1ST GENTLEMAN   This news, which is so like an old tale: has
                    the king found his heir?

3RD GENTLEMAN   Most true. Did you see the meeting of the
                    two kings?

2ND GENTLEMAN   No.

3RD GENTLEMAN   Then have you lost a sight! Our king being
                    ready to leap out of himself, for joy of his
                    found daughter, cries 'O, thy mother, thy
                    mother!' Then asks Polixenes forgiveness,
                    then embraces his son-in-law, now he
                    thanks the old shepherd.

4TH GENTLEMAN   The princess hearing of her mother's
                    statue – which is in the keeping of Paulina
                    – a piece many years in doing, by that rare
                    Italian master, Julio Romano – thither are
                    they gone.

1ST GENTLEMAN Let's along.

They depart, leaving Autolycus. The old shepherd and his son approach. They are splendidly dressed.

AUTOLYCUS Here come those I have done good to against my will. (*He bows to them.*) I humbly beseech you, sir, to pardon me all the faults I have committed.

SHEPHERD Prithee, son, do: for we must be gentle, now we are gentlemen.

SON Thou wilt amend thy life?

AUTOLYCUS Ay, and it like your good worship.

SON Come, follow us: we'll be thy good masters.

All are assembled in a chapel in Paulina's house. The statue of Hermione is hidden behind a curtain.

LEONTES O Paulina, we came to see the statue of our queen.

PAULINA Here it is. (*Draws back the curtain.*) Comes it not something near?

LEONTES   Her natural posture. Chide me, dear
             stone, that I may say indeed thou art
             Hermione. But yet, Paulina, Hermione
             was not so much wrinkled, nothing so
             aged as this seems.

POLIXENES   Oh, not by much.

PAULINA   So much the more our carver's excellence,
             which lets go by some sixteen years, and
             makes her as she liv'd now.

LEONTES   As now she might have done. Oh royal
             piece, there's magic in thy majesty.

PERDITA   (*kneeling*) Lady, dear queen, that ended
             when I but began, give me that hand of
             yours, to kiss.

PAULINA   O patience: the statue is but newly fix'd;
             the colour's not dry.

LEONTES   Let no man mock me, for I will kiss her.

PAULINA   Good my lord, forbear; the ruddiness
             upon her lip is wet: you'll mar it if you kiss
             it. Shall I draw the curtain?

LEONTES   No: not these twenty years.

PERDITA   So long could I stand by, a looker-on.

PAULINA   If you can behold it, I'll make the statue
            move indeed; descend, and take you by
            the hand. It is requir'd you do awake
            your faith. Music, awake her; strike;
            'tis time; descend; be stone no
            more; approach.

            The statue descends. It is Hermione herself.
            She is alive and holds out her hands to
            Leontes.

PAULINA   When she was young, you woo'd her: now,
            in age, is she become the suitor?

LEONTES   (*taking Hermione's hand*) Oh she's warm!
            If this be magic, let it be an art lawful
            as eating.

            Hermione embraces Leontes – silence descends
            as she hangs on his neck.

CAMILLO   If she pertain to life, let her speak too.

PAULINA   Mark a little while. (*To Perdita*) Please you
            to interpose, fair madam, kneel, and pray
            your mother's blessing; turn, good lady,
            our Perdita is found.

HERMIONE	(*crying, her tears falling as a heavenly blessing on her daughter*) You Gods look down, and from your sacred vials pour your graces upon my daughter's head! Tell me, mine own, where hast thou been preserv'd? where liv'd?
PAULINA	There's time enough for that. Go together, you precious winners all. I, an old turtle, will wing me to some wither'd bough, and there my mate, that's never to be found again, lament, till I am lost.
LEONTES	O peace, Paulina! Thou should'st a husband take by my consent, as I by thine a wife. Come, Camillo, and take her by the hand. Good Paulina, lead us from hence, where we may leisurely each one demand, and answer to his part perform'd in this wide gap of time, since first we were dissever'd.

The curtain falls.

King Richard III

King Richard III is the story of a royal monster, a misshapen devil by name of Richard, Duke of Gloucester. At the very beginning of the play, Shakespeare seems to hurl him onto the stage so that he limps and stumbles out of the shadows, almost unwillingly into the light. 'I am determined to prove a villain,' he confides; and does so with a vengeance as he claws his bloody way to the throne, murdering all who stand in his path, even little children: 'I fear no uncles dead,' says one of his nephews. 'Nor none that live, I hope,' protests his murderous uncle, and sends the child and his little brother to their deaths in the grim Tower of London. At length, even his own mother is driven to curse him: 'Bloody thou art, bloody will be thy end!' And so it is.

The Characters in the Play

in order of appearance

RICHARD	*Duke of Gloucester, later King Richard III*
THE DUKE OF CLARENCE	*his brother*
LADY ANNE	*widow of Edward, Prince of Wales*
TWO MURDERERS	
THE DUKE OF BUCKINGHAM	
QUEEN ELIZABETH	*wife to King Edward IV*
EDWARD	*Prince of Wales, her son*
THE DUKE OF YORK	*her younger son*
THE ARCHBISHOP OF YORK	
LORD HASTINGS	*the Lord Chamberlain*
LORD CARDINAL BOURCHIER	*The Archbishop of Canterbury*
SIR WILLIAM CATESBY	
THE BISHOP OF ELY	
THE DUCHESS OF YORK	*mother of Richard, Edward IV and the Duke of Clarence*
SIR JAMES TYRREL	
MESSENGER	
THE DUKE OF NORFOLK	
THE EARL OF RICHMOND	*afterwards King Henry VII Lords, soldiers, servants and attendants*

The curtain rises on the Palace of Westminster, dark against a bloodshot sky. A black misshapen figure crawls up onto the battlements and, like a malevolent spider, crouches over the town below.

RICHARD   Now is the winter of our discontent made
       glorious summer by this son of York.

       *The winter of discontent is the long civil war
       between the houses of York and Lancaster. The
       glorious son of York is the victor King Edward
       IV, and the speaker is his brother Richard, Duke
       of Gloucester.*

RICHARD   But I that am deform'd, unfinish'd, have no
       delight to pass away the time, and therefore,
       since I cannot prove a lover, I am
       determined to prove a villain . . .

       *King Edward is sick; and so is the kingdom.
       Fear, greed, treachery and hatred set family
       against family, mother against son, and brother
       against brother. A fierce ambition burns in the
       dark heart of the king's hunchback brother: he
       will be king! Already he has murdered Henry VI
       and his son, Edward, but others of his own
       family still stand in his way, even his brother
       George, Duke of Clarence.*

Along a stony passageway comes the Duke of Clarence, between armed guards. Suddenly the figure of Richard emerges from the darkness and stands in the way.

RICHARD   Brother, good day; what means this armed guard?

CLARENCE   His majesty hath appointed this conduct to convey me to the Tower.

RICHARD   Upon what cause?

CLARENCE   Because my name is George. A wizard told him that by 'G' his issue disinherited should be. And for my name of George begins with 'G', it follows in his thought that I am he.

RICHARD   Brother, farewell. I will unto the king. Your imprisonment shall not be long; I will deliver you, or else lie for you.

Clarence is marched away by the guard. Richard, smiling, stares after them. He rubs his hands with complicity.

RICHARD   Go, tread the path that thou shalt ne'er return; I do love thee so that I will shortly send thy soul to Heaven –

Richard is in his apartment, preening himself
before a mirror. He puts on his rings, admiring
the glitter of the precious stones. He is one step
nearer. But he needs to be respectable, he needs
a well-born wife, and who better than the
Lady Anne?

A noise outside attracts Richard's attention. He
sees from his window Lady Anne in mourning
and gentlemen with halberds, following a coffin.
The procession stops in front of his windows.

RICHARD   (*stepping back from the window*) I'll marry
Warwick's youngest daughter. What though I
kill'd her husband and her father?

ANNE   (*gazing at the coffin.*) Poor key-cold figure of
a holy king . . . be it lawful that I invocate
thy ghost to hear the lamentations of
poor Anne.

Suddenly a huge shadow falls over her. Anne
turns around. Richard appears in front of
the procession.

RICHARD   Villains, set down the corse!

The bearers lower the coffin and retreat in fear.

323

ANNE   Foul devil, for God's sake hence, and
                trouble us not.

RICHARD   Sweet saint, for charity, be not so curst.

ANNE   (*to bearers*) O gentlemen! see, see dead
                Henry's wounds open their congeal'd
                mouths and bleed afresh! Blush, blush thou
                lump of foul deformity, for 'tis thy presence
                that exhales this blood!

RICHARD   Lady, you know no rules of charity –

ANNE   Villain, thou know'st no law of God nor
                man! Didst thou not kill this king?

RICHARD   (*coming closer to Anne and speaking softly*) I
                grant ye. The better for the King of Heaven,
                that hath him.

ANNE   And thou unfit for any place but hell.

RICHARD   (*going around Anne*) Yes, one place else.

ANNE   Some dungeon?

RICHARD   (*stopping in front of Anne*) Your bed-chamber.

ANNE   (*spitting at him*) Out of my sight!

RICHARD	Your beauty was the cause, your beauty, that did haunt me in my sleep to undertake the death of all the world.

ANNE	(*covering her face with her hands*) If I thought that, I tell thee, homicide, these nails should rend that beauty from my cheeks.

RICHARD	Teach not thy lip such scorn; for it was made for kissing, lady, not for such contempt. If thy revengeful heart cannot forgive, lo, here I lend thee this sharp-pointed sword.

He kneels and, offering his sword, bares his breast. She takes the sword but, trembling, cannot strike the blow.

RICHARD	Nay, do not pause; for I did kill King Henry, but 'twas thy beauty that provoked me. Nay, now dispatch; 'twas I that stabb'd young Edward, but 'twas thy heavenly face that set me on. Take up the sword again, or take up me.

ANNE	I would I knew thy heart.

RICHARD	Vouchsafe to wear this ring.

Richard takes Anne's hand and puts a ring on her finger.

ANNE

To take is not to give.

RICHARD

Look how my ring encompasseth thy finger; even so thy breast encloseth my poor heart.

The procession departs, leaving Richard alone. He hops along, well pleased with himself, and his long misshapen shadow accompanies him.

RICHARD

(*to shadow*) Was ever woman in this humour woo'd? Was ever woman in this humour won? I'll have her, but I will not keep her long.

In the semi-darkness of King Edward's bedchamber the queen and relatives stand about his bed. Richard looks in and sees the queen make a few steps and kneel in front of a crucifix. The king's sickness has deepened and the queen is full of dread. Should he die, her sons are too young to rule. With George, Duke of Clarence, in the Tower, Richard, the third brother, will be Protector. And the venomous hunchback hates her and her family.

RICHARD

He cannot live, I hope, and must not die till George be pack'd with post-horse up to Heaven.

*In a small, gloomy room in the Tower, lit by
moonlight coming through the narrow windows,
the Duke of Clarence lies upon his bed. His sleep
is uneasy. Shadows fall across his face. He
wakes. Two murderers stare down on him.*

CLARENCE In God's name, what art thou?

1ST MURDERER A man, as you are.

CLARENCE Who sent you hither? Wherefore do
you come?

2ND MURDERER To –

CLARENCE To murder me? (*They nod.*) Wherein, my
friends have I offended you?

1ST MURDERER Offended us you have not, but the king;
therefore prepare to die.

CLARENCE I will send you to my brother Gloucester
who shall reward you better for my life than
Edward will for tidings of my death.

2ND MURDERER You are deceiv'd: your brother Gloucester
hates you.

1ST MURDERER 'Tis he that sends us to destroy you here.

He struggles from his bed and holds out his hands, pleadingly, to the second murderer. The first murderer stabs him, and pushes him head first into a malmsey-butt to drown in a nightmare of crimson bubbles.

A black flag flies above the palace. Richard has murdered his brother Clarence only just in time; King Edward is dead. All that remains between the hunchback and the crown is the problem of the king's two sons, the little princes. Desperately, the queen sends her own brothers to Ludlow to secure her children's safety, before it is too late. But Richard has a clever friend, his cousin, the Duke of Buckingham who advises they should not be tardy in seizing the heir to the throne.

BUCKINGHAM   My lord, whoever journeys to the prince, for God's sake let not us two stay at home.

RICHARD   My dear cousin, I as a child will go by thy direction. Towards Ludlow then.

The queen's brothers are seized by Richard's men and put to death and Edward, the little Prince of Wales, is brought to London. Hearing this terrible news, the queen decides to go with her younger son, the Duke of York, into sanctuary. Her friend, the Archbishop of York, leads them there.

ELIZABETH   (*clutching her youngest child*) Ay me! I see the ruin of our house: the tiger now hath seiz'd the gentle hind! Come, come, my boy; we will to sanctuary.

At the palace, Richard, Buckingham and others await the arrival of the Prince of Wales. As soon as he arrives, Richard, hopping and capering, like a genial uncle, comes forward to greet him. Buckingham follows Richard.

RICHARD   Welcome, dear cousin, the weary way hath made you melancholy.

EDWARD   No uncle; but our crosses on the way have made it tedious. (*He looks around him.*) I thought my mother and my brother York would long ere this have met us on the way. (*He turns to a nobleman, Lord Hastings.*) Welcome my lord. What, will our mother come?

HASTINGS   (*bowing*) The queen your mother and your brother York have taken sanctuary.

BUCKINGHAM   Fie, what an indirect and peevish course is this of hers! Lord Cardinal, will your grace persuade the queen to send the Duke of York unto his princely brother presently?

ARCHBISHOP   God in Heaven forbid we should infringe
              the sacred privilege of blessed sanctuary!

BUCKINGHAM   Oft have I heard of sanctuary men, but
              sanctuary children, never till now.

              The cardinal and Hastings leave.

EDWARD   Good lords, make all the speedy haste you
              may. (*To Richard*) Say, uncle Gloucester, if
              our brother come, where shall we sojourn
              till our coronation?

RICHARD   If I may counsel you, some day or
              two your Highness shall repose you at
              the Tower.

EDWARD   I do not like the Tower.

BUCKINGHAM   Now in good time here comes the Duke
              of York.

              *The young Duke of York, accompanied by
              Hastings and the cardinal, appears.*

EDWARD   Richard of York! how fares our loving
              brother?

YORK   Well, my lord.

RICHARD
How fares our cousin, noble lord of York?

YORK
I thank you, gentle uncle.

RICHARD
(*to Edward*) My lord, will't please you pass along? Myself will to your mother, to entreat of her to meet you at the Tower.

YORK
(*to his brother*) What, will you go unto the Tower, my lord?

EDWARD
My Lord Protector needs will have it so.

YORK
I shall not sleep in quiet at the Tower.

RICHARD
Why, what should you fear?

YORK
My uncle Clarence's angry ghost: my grandam told me he was murder'd there.

EDWARD
I fear no uncles dead.

RICHARD
Nor none that live, I hope?

The princes leave for the Tower that looms ahead, like a crouching monster. Richard and Buckingham stare after the procession. They see it disappear behind the gates of the fortress, the ravens circling above it. Richard rubs his hands with satisfaction.

With the two little princes, like birds in a cage, locked up in the Tower, Richard's way to the throne is clear. But before he can proclaim himself king, he needs the assent of Lord Hastings, the Lord Chamberlain.

BUCKINGHAM   What shall we do if we perceive Lord Hastings will not yield to our complots?

RICHARD   Chop off his head, man! (*He laughs and lays his arm upon Buckingham's shoulder.*) When I am king, claim thou of me the earldom of Hereford.

BUCKINGHAM   I'll claim that promise at your grace's hand.

In the middle of the night, Sir William Catesby, another friend of Richard's, is sent to rouse Lord Hastings from his bed and sound him out.

HASTINGS   What news, what news in this our tott'ring state?

CATESBY   It is a reeling world indeed, my lord, and will never stand upright till Richard wear the garland of the realm.

HASTINGS   Dost thou mean the crown?

CATESBY   Ay, my good lord.

HASTINGS   I'll have this crown of mine cut from my
           shoulders before I'll see the crown so
           foul misplac'd!

CATESBY   God keep your lordship in that gracious
           mind. (*He hides a grim smile.*)

           Lord Hastings is invited to dinner in the Tower.
           He supposes it is to fix the day for the crowning
           of little Prince Edward as England's rightful
           king. Why else should Richard, the Lord
           Protector, summon him? Seated at the table, he
           finds Ely, Buckingham and other nobles.

HASTINGS   Now, noble peers, the cause why we are met
           is to determine of the coronation. When is
           the royal day?

ELY   Tomorrow is I judge a happy day.

BUCKINGHAM Who knows the Lord Protector's mind
           herein?

ELY   Your grace, we think, should soonest know
           his mind.

BUCKINGHAM Lord Hastings, you and he are near in love.

HASTINGS   I thank his grace, I know he loves me well; but for his purpose in the coronation I have not sounded him. But you, my honourable lords, may name the time, and in the duke's behalf I'll give my voice –

ELY   In happy time, here comes the duke himself!

RICHARD   (*entering, all affable*) My noble lords and cousins all, good morrow!

BUCKINGHAM   Had you not come upon your cue, my lord, William, Lord Hastings had pronounc'd your part – I mean your voice for crowning of the king.

RICHARD   Than my Lord Hastings, no man might be bolder! My Lord of Ely, when I was last in Holborn I saw good strawberries in your garden there; I do beseech you, send for some of them!

ELY   Marry, and will, my lord, with all my heart! (*He leaves to send for some.*)

RICHARD   Cousin of Buckingham, a word with you. (*They leave the table together.*)

King Richard III

ELY   (*returning*) Where is the Duke of Gloucester?
             I have sent for these strawberries.

HASTINGS   His grace looks cheerfully and smooth this
             morning; there's some conceit or other likes
             him well. I think there's never a man in
             Christendom can lesser hide his love or hate
             than he, for by his face straight shall you
             know his heart.

             Richard returns with Buckingham.
             Buckingham is looking troubled,
             Richard savage.

RICHARD   I pray you all, tell me what they deserve
             that do conspire my death with devilish
             plots of damned witchcraft, and that have
             prevail'd upon my body with their
             hellish charms?

HASTINGS   I say, my lord, they have deserved death.

RICHARD   Then be your eyes the witness of their evil!
             (*Drags up a sleeve to show his withered arm.*)
             See how I am bewitch'd! And this is
             Edward's wife, that monstrous witch,
             consorted with that harlot, strumpet
             Shore, that by their witchcraft thus have
             marked me!

335

HASTINGS   If they have done this deed, my noble lord –

RICHARD   If? Thou protector of this damned strumpet, talk'st thou to me of ifs? Thou art a traitor: off with his head! Now by Saint Paul I will not dine until I see the same.

Richard storms out, and is followed by the others, leaving the dismayed Hastings. Two sinister figures of the guard appear behind him. One of them puts his hand on Hastings' shoulder and squeezes it. Hastings lowers his head realizing that he is doomed. He is led away.

A servant enters the room bearing a dish of strawberries that he places on the table. The other nobles return with Richard and Buckingham. They seat themselves and dishes are brought in. A covered plate is set before Richard. He lifts the lid. Hastings' severed head glares out. Silence falls upon the table.

RICHARD   (*sighing*) So dear I lov'd the man that I must weep. (*He bows his head.*)

BUCKINGHAM   (*jumping up*) Long live King Richard, England's worthy king!

LORDS   Long live King Richard!

At last the hunchback, having climbed a ladder of murders, is king. But while he walks in glory, three women stand in wretchedness and grief before the Tower. Richard's unhappy wife, the Lady Anne; the queen, mother of the two little princes; and the mother of the hunchback himself, the Duchess of York.

DUCHESS   O my accursed womb, the bed of death! A cockatrice hast thou hatch'd to the world, whose unavoided eye is murderous!

ANNE   He hates me . . . and will, no doubt, shortly be rid of me.

QUEEN   Pity, you ancient stones, those tender babes. Rough cradle for such little pretty ones! Use my babies well.

In the great hall of the palace, thronged with nobles, King Richard, crowned and robed, hops between the bowing figures. His cloak is huge and scarlet and flows after him like a river of blood. He ascends the throne and beckons to Buckingham who comes to kneel beside him.

RICHARD   Shall we wear these glories for a day? Or shall they last?

BUCKINGHAM   For ever let them last!

RICHARD   (*shaking his head*) Young Edward lives –
                   think now what I would speak.

BUCKINGHAM   Say on, my loving lord.

RICHARD   Cousin, thou wast not wont to be so dull.
                   Shall I be plain? I wish the bastards dead.
                   What say'st thou now?

BUCKINGHAM   Your grace may do your pleasure.

RICHARD   Tut, tut, thou art all ice. Say, have I thy
                   consent that they shall die?

BUCKINGHAM   Give me some little breath, some pause,
                   before I positively speak in this.

                   *Bowing, Buckingham withdraws. Richard stares
                   after him, malevolently.*

RICHARD   High-reaching Buckingham grows
                   circumspect. (*He beckons to a page, who
                   approaches. Richard murmurs in his ear.*)
                   Know'st thou not any whom corrupting gold
                   will tempt unto a close exploit of death?
                   (*The page nods and hastens away. Richard
                   glares about him. He sees Buckingham smiling.
                   He smiles in return.*) No more shall he be
                   neighbour to my counsels. Come hither,
                   Catesby! Rumour it abroad that Anne, my

338

wife, is very grievous sick. (*Catesby looks startled.*) I say again, give out that Anne, my queen, is sick and like to die. About it! (*Catesby departs.*)

In his bedchamber, Richard frowns into the mirror. To keep the crown he's seized, he needs a better marriage. Once rid of Anne, he will marry Elizabeth, sister of the two little princes who still languish in the Tower.

The page enters, accompanied by a desperate, needy-looking gentleman by the name of Sir James Tyrrel. Richard gestures for the page to leave.

RICHARD Dar'st thou resolve to kill a friend of mine?

TYRREL Please you, but I had rather kill two enemies.

RICHARD Why then thou hast it; two deep enemies. Tyrrel, I mean those bastards in the Tower.

TYRREL I will dispatch it straight! (*He hastens away. No sooner has he left than Buckingham enters.*)

BUCKINGHAM My lord, I have consider'd in my mind the late request that you did sound me in.

RICHARD   (*with an airy wave of his hand*) Well, let
           that rest.

BUCKINGHAM   My lord, I claim the gift, my due by
              promise, th' earldom of Hereford –

RICHARD   (*as if not hearing*) I do remember me, Henry
           the Sixth did prophesy that Richmond
           should be king, when Richmond was a little
           peevish boy.

BUCKINGHAM   My lord, your promise for the earldom!

RICHARD   I am not in the giving vein today. Thou
           troublest me; I am not in the vein. (*Richard
           moves away, leaving Buckingham red-faced
           and alone.*)

BUCKINGHAM   And is it thus? Repays he my deep service
              with such contempt? Made I him king or this?
              O, let me think on Hastings, and be gone!

              *If Buckingham had proved a broken reed, Tyrrel
              was made of sterner stuff. With the help of two
              sturdy assistants, he smothers the two children
              while they sleep.*

              *In the royal apartments, Richard, surrounded
              by servants, attires himself splendidly in front of
              a mirror.*

RICHARD   The sons of Edward sleep in Abraham's bosom, and Anne my wife hath bid this world good night. Now, for I know that Richmond aims at young Elizabeth, my brother's daughter, and by that knot looks proudly on the crown – to her go I, a jolly thriving wooer. (*Richard hops but suddenly Catesby stands in his path.*)

RICHARD   (*with irritation*) Good or bad news, that thou com'st in so bluntly?

CATESBY   Bad news, my lord: Ely is fled to Richmond, and Buckingham, back'd with the hardy Welshmen, is in the field, and still his power increaseth.

RICHARD   (*clenching his fists*) Go, muster men. We must be brief, when traitors brave the field.

But the news goes from bad to worse.

MESSENGER   My lord, the army of great Buckingham is –

RICHARD   Out on you, owls! Nothing but songs of death? (*He strikes him. The messenger falls down.*) There, take thou that, till thou bring better news!

MESSENGER	(*getting up*) The news I have to tell your majesty is that by sudden flood and fall of water Buckingham's army is dispers'd and scatter'd, and he himself wander'd away alone.
RICHARD	I cry thee mercy; there is my purse to cure that blow of thine. (*He flings some money at him.*)
CATESBY	My liege, the Duke of Buckingham is taken: that is the best news. That the Earl of Richmond is with a mighty power landed at Milford is colder tidings, yet they must be told.
RICHARD	Away towards Salisbury! While we reason here, a royal battle might be won and lost!

Outside the palace, Richard is setting forth at the head of his army. Trumpets blaze, drums roar. On the bridge, he is confronted by two raging women: his mother, the Duchess of York, and the queen. The music ceases.

| QUEEN | Tell me, thou villain-slave, where are my children? |
| DUCHESS | Thou toad, thou toad, where is thy brother Clarence? |

At a sign from Richard, music strikes up, and the duchess' voiced is drowned. At another sign, it ceases.

RICHARD   Be patient and entreat me fair, and brief, good mother, for I am in haste.

DUCHESS   Art thou so hasty? I have stay'd for thee, God knows, in torment and in agony.

RICHARD   And came I not at last to comfort you?

DUCHESS   Thou cam'st on earth to make the earth my hell! Therefore take with thee my most grievous curse, which in the day of battle tire thee more than all the complete armour that thou wear'st! Bloody thou art, bloody will be thy end; shame serves thy life and doth thy death attend!

The two women turn and stalk away, their robes flapping like birds of ill-omen. Richard laughs and rides away.

Though he is beset by troubles, the hunchback king does not forget his friends. He gives orders for the Duke of Buckingham to be put to death. Like the good politician he is, he knows the importance of detail and when his camp is pitched on Bosworth field, he is everywhere spying out weaknesses. Now he is prepared for battle.

RICHARD   Here will I lie tonight – But where tomorrow? Well, all's one for that!

It is night. Richard is alone in his tent. The lamp flickers on the table and his armour lies on the floor, like a dead king. He remembers his mother's curse.

Richard goes to the entrance of his tent and speaks to his officers.

RICHARD   Stir with the lark tomorrow, gentle Norfolk.

NORFOLK   I warrant you, my lord.

RICHARD   *(to another officer)* Give me a bowl of wine. I have not that alacrity of spirit nor cheer of mind that I was wont to have. Leave me.

Richard is alone in his tent. He sits wearily down on his bed and drinks a glass of wine in one gulp. He puts the glass on the table and watches the light of the lamp. He sleeps. The lamp begins to burn blue. Strange, flimsy white wisps enter the tent. They gather round the sleeping king. Little by little, they assume more definite shapes. They are the ghosts of his

victims. They go in circles above Richard, one by
one coming closer to him. Richards stirs and
tosses in his sleep.

GHOST OF
CLARENCE   Poor Clarence, by thy guile betray'd to
death – tomorrow in the battle think on me.

ALL GHOSTS   Despair and die!

GHOST OF
HASTINGS   In a bloody battle end thy days! Think on
Lord Hastings!

ALL GHOSTS   Despair and die!

GHOSTS OF TWO
LITTLE PRINCES   Dream on thy cousins smother'd in
the Tower.

ALL GHOSTS   Despair and die!

GHOST OF ANNE   Richard, thy wife, that wretched Anne, thy
wife. Tomorrow in the battle think on me.

ALL GHOSTS   Despair and die!

GHOST OF
BUCKINGHAM   The first was I that help'd thee to the
crown; the last was I that felt thy tyranny. O,

in the battle think of Buckingham, and die
in terror of thy guiltiness.

Richard awakes and looks around him in terror.

RICHARD   Soft, I did but dream. What do I fear?
               Myself? (*He sees his huge shadow on the wall
               of the tent and smiles at it.*) Richard loves
               Richard: that is, I and I. Is there a murderer
               here? (*He draws his dagger.*) No. Yes, I am.
               Then fly. What, from myself?

*Richard pours wine into a goblet. His hands are
shaking. He spills some wine, which spreads like
a pool of blood over the table. He drinks the
wine in one gulp.*

RICHARD   Let not our babbling dreams affright our
               souls; conscience is but a word that cowards
               use, devis'd at first to keep the strong in awe.
               Our strong arms be our conscience, swords
               our law.

Richard is himself again.

*On the hillside, in the early morning mist,
Richard, on his great white horse, rides up
and down before his troops. He looks up to
the sky.*

RICHARD   The sun will not be seen today. Not shine
                 today? Why, what is that to me more than
                 to Richmond?

                 *He looks towards the place where Richmond's
                 troops are waiting. Suddenly a sun-ray cuts
                 through the clouds. Richmond's armour flares
                 up in gold. He is ahead of his troops.*

NORFOLK   (*riding up to Richard*) Arm, arm, my lord; the
                 foe vaunts in the field!

RICHARD   Come, bustle, bustle! (*He addresses his
                 troops.*) March on! Join bravely. Let us to it
                 pell-mell, if not to Heaven, then hand in
                 hand to hell! Fight, gentlemen of England!
                 Fight, bold yeomen! Draw, archers, draw
                 your arrows to the head. Advance, our
                 standards. Set upon our foes!

                 *He waves, and the advance begins, down the
                 hillside towards the enemy. Richard's troops
                 mingle with Richmond's troops in battle,
                 Richard laying about him like a madman. At
                 last, his horse is killed. He scrambles to his feet
                 and fights on.*

RICHARD   A horse! A horse! My kingdom for
                 a horse!

Catesby rides by.

CATESBY   Withdraw, my lord. I'll help you to
a horse.

RICHARD   Slave, I have set my life upon a cast, and I
will stand the hazard of the die! I think there
be six Richmonds in the field: five have I
slain today instead of him!

*He stumbles away, killing and killing. Suddenly
he confronts the tall, golden figure of Richmond.
He raises his sword. The air is full of whispers.
He strikes out, but his sword is heavy.
Richmond in a single blow cuts off
Richard's head.*

*The crown is brought to Richmond. He puts it
on and all kneel before him.*

RICHMOND   (*staring around the battlefield that is littered
with the dead*) England hath long been mad
and scarr'd herself: the brother blindly shed
the brother's blood; the father rashly
slaughter'd his own son; the son, compell'd,
been butcher to the sire. All this divided
York and Lancaster – O, now let Richmond
and Elizabeth, the true succeeders of each
royal house, by God's fair ordinance conjoin
together! Now civil wounds are stopp'd,

peace lives again. That she may long live
here, God say amen!

The curtain falls.

The Tempest

This must be the strangest and most mysterious of Shakespeare's plays: peopled by monsters, spirits, clowns, lovers and villains, it begins with a magical tempest, and ends in a magical calm. It tells the story of Prospero, Duke of Milan, who has been overthrown by his wicked brother and, together with his baby daughter, cast adrift in an open boat. Together, they drift across the seas until they come ashore upon a strange, enchanted island. There, with the aid of magical books saved from his library, he becomes a great enchanter and subdues the weird inhabitants of the isle, chief among whom are Ariel, a discontented spirit, and Caliban, a savage and deformed slave. Then, one day, his enemies come within his power. He raises a tempest and wrecks their vessel on the island's shore. Now they are at his mercy . . .

Shakespeare wrote it when he was about forty-seven, and it seems to have been his last completed play. It was probably influenced by the account of a shipwreck on the island of Bermuda that had been published in the previous year; but, apart from that, it owes little to any known source. Its magic is all Shakespeare's own.

350

Indeed, like *A Midsummer Night's Dream, The Tempest* is much concerned with the power of illusion, which extends to all reality and existence itself. 'The cloud-capped towers, the gorgeous palaces, the solemn temples, the great globe itself, yea, all which it inherit, shall dissolve,' prophesies Prospero, 'and like this insubstantial pageant faded leave not a rack behind. We are such stuff as dreams are made on . . .'

As this was Shakespeare's last completed play, many people have seen it as his farewell to his art; but surely he could not have known that it was to be his last work; so is it not better to see it as 'something rich and strange', marking, not an ending, but the way onwards, towards something new?

The Characters in the Play

in order of appearance

VOICE(S)	*of mariners*
MIRANDA	*daughter to Prospero*
PROSPERO	*the right Duke of Milan*
ARIEL	*an airy spirit*
CALIBAN	*a savage and deformed slave*
FERDINAND	*son to the King of Naples*
GONZALO	*an honest old councillor*
ALONSO	*King of Naples*
SEBASTIAN	*brother to the King of Naples*
ANTONIO	*the usurping Duke of Milan, brother to Prospero*
TRINCULO	*a jester*
STEPHANO	*a drunken butler*
(IRIS)	
JUNO	*spirits*
CERES	
BOATSWAIN	

(Names in brackets indicate non-speaking parts)

The curtain rises on Prospero's isle, a strange, uninhabited place, mysterious with mists, and set in the midst of a glassy sea. The lord of the isle, clad in his magic mantle, stands upon a promontory with his arm about his daughter, Miranda. Together, they gaze out towards a distant ship. Prospero's eyes are glittering.

At last, after twelve long years on the haunted isle, his enemies are within his grasp: his wicked brother Antonio, Alonso, the greedy King of Naples, and his treacherous brother Sebastian; even Gonzalo, the kindly courtier who, when he and his tiny daughter had been set adrift in a rotting boat, had secretly provided them with food and clothing, and those precious books from his library that had turned the poor, betrayed Duke of Milan into Prospero, the mighty enchanter.

He raises the carved staff he holds in his right hand, and stretches out towards the distant ship. At once, a black cloud appears in the clear sky. It assumes a wild and savage shape, and pounces on the vessel. It is full of dazzling worms of lightning, and the vessel heaves and twists in a vain effort to escape. Tiny shouts and screams reach the silent onlookers.

VOICES   We split, we split!

A VOICE   Hell is empty and all the devils are here!

                The ship's company leap overboard; then the black cloud obscures all. When it has dispersed, the sea is glassy again. The vessel has vanished.

MIRANDA   Poor souls, they perished!

PROSPERO	Be collected: no more amazement: tell your piteous heart there's no harm done.
MIRANDA	O, woe the day!
PROSPERO	No harm. I have done nothing but in care of thee.

He seats himself; she sits beside him. Fondly, he strokes her hair, then gently touches her eyes.

| PROSPERO | Thou art inclined to sleep. |

Miranda sleeps. Prospero rises and paces the sands.

| PROSPERO | Come away, servant come. I am ready now. Approach, my Ariel, come! |

A strange creature manifests itself out of the air, a bright, trembling, vague creature, neither beast nor human, but endlessly changing between them.

ARIEL	All hail, great master! Grave sir, hail!
PROSPERO	Hast thou, spirit, performed to point the tempest that I bade thee?
ARIEL	(*proudly*) To every article! I boarded the King's ship, now on the beak, now in the waist, in every cabin, I flamed amazement!

PROSPERO   My brave spirit!

ARIEL   Not a soul but felt a fever of the mad, and
played some tricks of desperation!

PROSPERO   But are they, Ariel, safe?

ARIEL   Not a hair perished! In troops I have dispersed
them 'bout the isle. The King's son I have
landed by himself.

PROSPERO   Why, that's my spirit! But there's more work –

ARIEL   What, more toil?

PROSPERO   How now? Moody? What is't thou canst
demand?

ARIEL   My liberty.

PROSPERO   Before the time be out? No more! Dost thou
forget from what a torment I did free thee?

ARIEL   Pardon, master, I will be correspondent to
command and do my spiriting gently.

PROSPERO   Do so; and after two days I will discharge thee.

ARIEL   That's my noble master! What shall I do? say
what? what shall I do?

PROSPERO   Go make thyself like a nymph o'the sea, be
             subject to no sight but thine and mine, invisible
             to every eyeball else. (*Instantly, Ariel, with a
             flurry of strange gestures, becomes a sea-nymph,
             lovely and delicate.*) Fine apparition! My quaint
             Ariel, hark in thine ear. (*He whispers in
             Ariel's ear*).

ARIEL   My lord, it shall be done. (*He vanishes.*)

             Prospero returns to the sleeping Miranda.

PROSPERO   Awake, dear heart, awake! Thou hast slept well.
             (*Miranda wakes.*) Come on, we'll visit Caliban,
             my slave –

MIRANDA   'Tis a villain, sir, I do not love to look on.

PROSPERO   But as 'tis we cannot miss him: he does make
             our fire, fetch in our wood. (*Together, they walk to
             the entrance of a cave.*) What, ho! Slave! Caliban!
             Thou earth, thou! Come forth!

             *With much groaning, Caliban, a monstrous,
             deformed creature, crawls out.*

CALIBAN   A south-west blow on ye and blister you all o'er!

PROSPERO   For this, be sure, tonight thou shalt have cramps,
             side-stitches that shall pen thy breath up –

CALIBAN   I must eat my dinner. This island's mine, by
Sycorax my mother, which thou tak'st from me.
When thou cam'st first, thou strok'st me and
made much of me, would'st give me water with
berries in't, and teach me how to name the
bigger light, and how the less, that burn by day
and night; and then I loved thee –

PROSPERO   Thou most lying slave, whom stripes may move,
not kindness! I have used thee, filth as thou art,
with human care; and lodged thee in mine own
cell, till thou didst seek to violate the honour of
my child.

CALIBAN   O, ho, O, ho! Would't had been done! Thou
did'st prevent me; I had peopled else this isle
with Calibans!

PROSPERO   Hag-seed, hence! Fetch us in fuel!

CALIBAN   (*creeping away*) I must obey. His art is of
such power . . .

*Another part of the island. The sea-shore.
Ferdinand, the king's son, saved from the sea,
walks warily. The invisible Ariel leads him with
a song:*

ARIEL   Come unto these yellow sands,
And then take hands:

357

Curtsied when you have, and kissed,
The wild waves whist . . .

FERDINAND   Where should this music be? I'th'air or th'earth?

ARIEL   Full fathom five thy father lies;
Of his bones are coral made;
Those are pearls that were his eyes:
Nothing of him that doth fade,
But doth suffer a sea-change
Into something rich and strange . . .

FERDINAND   The ditty does remember my drowned father.

*Little by little, the singing, invisible Ariel
leads Ferdinand into the presence of Prospero
and Miranda.*

MIRANDA   What is't? A spirit?

PROSPERO   No, wench; it eats and sleeps and has such
senses as we have – such. This gallant which
thou seest was in the wreck. He hath lost his
fellows and strays about to find 'em.

MIRANDA   I might call him a thing divine; for nothing
natural I ever saw so noble!

*Even as Miranda stares in wonderment at
Ferdinand, so does he stare at the girl.*

FERDINAND	Most sure the goddess on whom these airs attend! O you wonder! If you be maid or no?

MIRANDA	No wonder, sir; but certainly a maid.

FERDINAND	My language! heavens! I am the best of them that speak this speech, were I but where 'tis spoken.

PROSPERO	(*aside*) At first sight they have changed eyes! Delicate Ariel, I'll set thee free for this! (*To Ferdinand*) How? the best? What wert thou, if the King of Naples heard thee? A word, good sir, I fear you have done yourself some wrong: a word.

MIRANDA	Why speaks my father so ungently? This is the third man that e'er I saw; the first that e'er I sighed for –

FERDINAND	O, if a virgin, and your affection not gone forth, I'll make you the Queen of Naples!

PROSPERO	I charge thee: thou dost here usurp the name thou ow'st not; and hast put thyself upon this island as a spy, to win it from me, the lord on't.

FERDINAND	No, as I am a man!

PROSPERO   (*Miranda moves to defend Ferdinand*) Speak not
            you for him: he's a traitor. Come, I'll manacle
            thy neck and feet together –

FERDINAND   No; I will resist –

            *He draws his sword. Prospero raises his staff, and
            Ferdinand finds his arm frozen. Desperately,
            Miranda clutches at her father's mantle.*

PROSPERO   Hence! Hang not on my garments!

MIRANDA   Sir, have pity! I'll be his surety!

PROSPERO   What! An advocate for an impostor! Hush!
            Thou thinkest there is no more shapes such as
            he, having seen but him and Caliban: foolish
            wench! To th'most of men this is a Caliban, and
            they to him are angels.

MIRANDA   My affections are most humble; I have no
            ambition to see a goodlier man.

PROSPERO   (*to Ferdinand*) Come on, obey!

MIRANDA   Be of comfort; my father's of a better nature, sir,
            than he appears . . .

PROSPERO   (*aside to Ariel, who has been hovering,
            invisible*) Thou shalt be as free as mountain

winds; but then exactly do all points of
my command . . .

*A woodland glade, in which the chief survivors of the
wreck now find themselves; Alonso, King of Naples;
Sebastian, his brother; Antonio, brother to Prospero;
Gonzalo, the kindly courtier who had once assisted
Prospero and his daughter; and other attending
lords. They are plainly weary from walking.*

GONZALO   Beseech you, sir, be merry; you have cause, so
have we all, of joy; for our escape is much
beyond our loss –

ALONSO   Prithee, peace.

SEBASTIAN   (*to Antonio*) He receives comfort like
cold porridge.

GONZALO   The air breathes upon us here most sweetly –

SEBASTIAN   As if it had lungs, and rotten ones.

GONZALO   Our garments, being as they were, drenched in
the sea, seem now as fresh as when we were at
Tunis at the marriage of your daughter who is
now Queen.

ALONSO   Would I had never married my daughter there!
For, coming thence, my son is lost. O thou mine

heir of Naples and Milan, what strange fish hath made his meal on thee?

GONZALO   Sir, he may live; I saw him beat the surges under him –

ALONSO   No, no, he's gone.

SEBASTIAN   Sir, you may thank yourself for this great loss, that would not bless our Europe with your daughter –

ALONSO   Prithee, peace.

SEBASTIAN   The fault's your own!

GONZALO   My lord Sebastian, the truth you speak doth lack some gentleness. You rub the sore when you should bring the plaster.

Ariel appears above, hovering invisibly; and makes strange signs in the air. Gonzalo, the king and the attendant lords become suddenly drowsy. They settle on the ground.

GONZALO   You are ... gentlemen of – of ... I am very heavy.

ANTONIO   Go sleep. (*Gonzalo sleeps.*)

ALONSO   I wish mine eyes would, with themselves, shut

my thoughts . . . (*He yawns.*) I find they are
inclined to do so.

*The king sleeps, and following his example so do all,
except for Sebastian and Antonio.*

SEBASTIAN   What a strange drowsiness possesses them!

ANTONIO   It is the quality o'th'climate.

SEBASTIAN   I find not myself disposed to sleep.

ANTONIO   Nor I.

*Antonio glances at the sleeping king, and then looks
meaningly at Sebastian.*

ANTONIO   What might, worthy Sebastian? – O what might?
My strong imagination sees a crown dropping
upon thy head.

SEBASTIAN   Prithee, say on.

ANTONIO   Will you grant with me that Ferdinand
is drowned?

SEBASTIAN   He's gone.

ANTONIO   Then tell me, who's the next heir to Naples?

SEBASTIAN   Claribel.

ANTONIO   She that is Queen of Tunis; she that dwells ten leagues beyond man's life. (*He nods towards the sleeping king.*) What a sleep were this for your advancement! Do you understand me?

SEBASTIAN   Methinks I do. I remember you did supplant your brother Prospero.

ANTONIO   True: and look how well my garments sit upon me.

SEBASTIAN   Thy case, dear friend, shall be my precedent; as thou got'st Milan, I'll come by Naples. Draw thy sword!

The friends creep upon the sleepers with drawn swords, ready to murder the king and Gonzalo. Swiftly, Ariel descends.

ARIEL   (*in Gonzalo's ear*) Awake, awake!

The sleepers awake, and see Sebastian and Antonio with drawn swords.

ALONSO   Why, how now? Why are you drawn?

GONZALO   What's the matter?

SEBASTIAN   We heard a hollow burst of bellowing, like bulls, or rather lions!

ALONSO   I heard nothing.

ANTONIO   Sure, it was a roar of a whole herd of lions!

ALONSO   Heard you this, Gonzalo?

GONZALO   Upon mine honour, sir, I heard a humming – there was a noise, that's verily.

ALONSO   Lead off this ground; and let's make further search for my poor son.

They all rise and leave the glade, watched by Ariel.

Another part of the island. Enter Caliban, bearing heavy logs for firewood on his back.

CALIBAN   All the infections that the sun sucks up from bogs, fens, flats, on Prosper fall, and make him by inch-meal, a disease . . .

Trinculo, the king's jester, who has also escaped the wreck enters. In his clown's motley, he presents a strange sight.

CALIBAN   Lo, now lo! Here comes a spirit of his, and to

torment me for bringing wood in slowly. I'll fall
flat; perchance he will not mind me!

*Caliban falls flat, and covers himself with his rough
cloak. He lies motionless. Trinculo stumbles over
him. Cautiously he investigates.*

TRINCULO   What have we here? A man or a fish? Dead or
alive? A fish: he smells like a fish; a very ancient
and fish-like smell. (*He feels under the cloak.*)
Warm, o'my troth! This is no fish, but an
islander, who hath lately suffered by a
thunder-bolt!

There is a loud peal of thunder.

Alas, the storm is come again! My best way is to
creep under his gaberdine; there is no other
shelter hereabout: misery acquaints a man with
strange bed-fellows!

*He creeps under the cloak and settles down, so that
his legs and Caliban's protrude at opposite ends.
Now comes yet another survivor. It is Stephano, the
king's butler. As always he is clutching a bottle and
is drunk. He sings.*

STEPHANO   I shall no more to sea, to sea
Here shall I die ashore . . .

This is a very scurvy tune to sing at a man's
funeral; here's my comfort!

*He drinks, and kicks accidentally against the
combined Caliban–Trinculo.*

CALIBAN   Do not torment me – O!

Stephano investigates the four-legged cloak.

STEPHANO   This is some monster of the isle with four legs,
who hath got, as I take it, an ague. Where the
devil should he learn our language?

CALIBAN   Do not torment me, prithee; I'll bring my wood
home faster.

STEPHANO   He is in his fit now, and does not talk after the
wisest. He shall taste of my bottle. Come on
your ways; open your mouth –

*He thrusts the bottle under the cloak, and there is a
noise of gulping.*

TRINCULO   I should know that voice: it should be – but he
is drowned!

STEPHANO   Four legs and two voices! Amen! I will pour
some in thy other mouth!

TRINCULO   Stephano! If thou beest Stephano, touch me, and speak to me; for I am Trinculo!

STEPHANO   If thou beest Trinculo, come forth!

Trinculo comes forth. He and Stephano stare at one another; and then, in an access of joy, Trinculo seizes Stephano and whirls him round in a dance.

TRINCULO   O Stephano, two Neapolitans 'scaped!

STEPHANO   Prithee, do not turn me about; my stomach is not constant.

CALIBAN   (*emerging*) That's a brave god, and bears celestial liquor. I will kneel to him.

STEPHANO   How didst thou 'scape? I escaped upon a butt of sack, which the sailors heaved o'erboard.

TRINCULO   O Stephano, hast any more of this?

STEPHANO   The whole butt, man.

CALIBAN   Hast thou not dropped from heaven?

The two friends, as if for the first time, see Caliban kneeling.

STEPHANO   Out o'the moon, I do assure thee. I was the man i'the moon . . .

CALIBAN   I have seen thee in her, and I do adore thee!

STEPHANO   Come, swear to that; kiss the book. (*He proffers the bottle.*)

TRINCULO   This is a very shallow monster! The man i'th'moon! A most poor credulous monster!

CALIBAN   I will kiss thy foot; I prithee, be my god.

TRINCULO   I shall laugh myself to death at this puppy-headed monster! I could find in my heart to beat him –

STEPHANO   Come, kiss!

TRINCULO   – but that the poor monster's in drink!

CALIBAN   (*rising*) I'll show thee the best springs; I'll pluck thee berries; I'll fish for thee, and get thee wood enough. A plague upon the tyrant that I serve!

TRINCULO   A most ridiculous monster, to make a wonder of a poor drunkard!

STEPHANO   I prithee now, lead the way. Trinculo, the King and all our company else being drowned, we will inherit here!

Caliban takes up his burden of logs, and staggering drunkenly, leads the way and sings as he goes:

CALIBAN
'Ban, 'Ban, Cacaliban,
Has a new master: – get a new man!
Freedom, high-day! high-day, freedom!
Freedom, high-day, freedom!

Before Prospero's cell. Ferdinand, a prisoner, staggers under the weight of a log that he bears from one pile to another. As he toils, Miranda slips out of the cell.

MIRANDA
Alas now, pray you, work not so hard. My father is hard at study; pray, now, rest yourself. He's safe for these three hours.

Prospero watches Miranda and Ferdinand from concealment. He smiles to himself.

PROSPERO
Poor worm, thou art infected.

MIRANDA
You look wearily.

FERDINAND
No, noble mistress: 'tis fresh morning with me when you are by at night. What is your name?

MIRANDA
Miranda.

FERDINAND
Admired Miranda! Indeed the top of admiration! Hear my soul speak: the very

370

instant that I saw you, did my heart fly to
your service!

MIRANDA   Do you love me?

FERDINAND O heaven, O earth, bear witness! I, beyond all
limit of what else i'th'world, do love, prize,
honour you!

MIRANDA   I am a fool to weep at what I am glad of.

PROSPERO   Fair encounter of two most rare affections!
Heavens rain grace on that which breeds
between 'em!

FERDINAND Wherefore weep you?

MIRANDA   At mine unworthiness, that dare not offer what
I desire to give. I am your wife if you will marry
me; if not, I'll die your maid.

FERDINAND My mistress, dearest –

MIRANDA   My husband, then?

FERDINAND Ay, with a heart as willing as bondage e'er of
freedom. Here's my hand.

MIRANDA   And mine, with my heart in't. And now farewell
till half an hour hence.

A forest clearing, in which Stephano has laid up his wine barrel. King-like, he sits upon it. Trinculo stands beside him, and Caliban lays his burden of firewood at his new master's feet. Stephano holds out his bottle.

STEPHANO   Servant-monster, drink to me!

TRINCULO   Servant-monster! The folly of this island! They say there's but five upon this isle: we are three of them; if th' other two be brain'd like us, the state totters.

CALIBAN   (*drinking*) How does thy honour? Let me lick thy shoe. I'll not serve him, he is not valiant.

TRINCULO   Thou liest, most ignorant monster!

STEPHANO   Trinculo, keep a good tongue in your head: if you prove a mutineer, – the next tree!

CALIBAN   I thank my noble lord. As I told thee before, I am subject to a tyrant, a sorcerer, that by his cunning hath cheated me of the island.

Ariel, as ever, invisible to all, appears and stands behind Trinculo.

ARIEL   (*in Trinculo's voice*) Thou liest!

CALIBAN   Thou liest, thou jesting monkey, thou! I would
           my valiant master would destroy thee, I do
           not lie.

STEPHANO   Trinculo, if you trouble him any more in's tale,
           by this hand, I will supplant some of your teeth!

TRINCULO   Why, I said nothing.

CALIBAN   I say, by sorcery he got this isle; from me he got
           it. If thy greatness will revenge it on him, thou
           shalt be lord of it, and I'll serve thee.

STEPHANO   How now shall this be compassed?

CALIBAN   I'll yield him to thee asleep, where thou mayst
           knock a nail into his head.

ARIEL   (*in Trinculo's voice*) Thou liest: thou canst not.

CALIBAN   What a pied ninny's this! Thou scurvy patch!

TRINCULO   Why, what did I? I did nothing.

ARIEL   (*in Trinculo's voice*) Thou liest.

STEPHANO   Take thou that! (*He beats Trinculo furiously.
           Trinculo retires in tears. Caliban claps his hands in
           delight.*) Now, forward with your tale.

373

CALIBAN   'Tis a custom with him in the afternoon to
           sleep: there thou mayst brain him having first
           seized his books. Remember, first to possess his
           books; for without them he's but a sot, as I am.
           Burn but his books. And that most deeply to
           consider is the beauty of his daughter; he
           himself calls her a nonpareil.

STEPHANO   Is it so brave a lass?

CALIBAN   Ay, lord, she will become thy bed, I warrant, and
           bring thee forth brave brood.

STEPHANO   Monster, I will kill this man: his daughter and I
           will be king and queen – save our graces! – and
           Trinculo and thyself shall be viceroys. Dost thou
           like the plot, Trinculo?

TRINCULO   Excellent!

STEPHANO   Give me thy hand, I am sorry I beat thee; but
           while thou liv'st, keep a good tongue in thy head.

CALIBAN   Within this half hour he will be asleep. Wilt thou
           destroy him then?

ARIEL   This will I tell my master. (*Ariel plays
           strange music.*)

TRINCULO   (*frightened*) O forgive me my sins!

374

STEPHANO   (*boldly*) He that dies pays all debts. I defy thee.
            Mercy upon us!

            He strikes at the air, wildly, as the music seems to
            taunt them.

CALIBAN   Be not afeared; the isle is full of noises, sounds
            and sweet airs, that give delight and hurt not.
            Sometimes a thousand twangling instruments
            will hum about mine ears; and sometimes
            voices, that if I then had waked after long sleep,
            will make me sleep again, and then in dreaming,
            the clouds methought would open, and show
            riches ready to drop upon me, that when I
            waked, I cried to dream again.

STEPHANO   This will prove a brave kingdom to me, where I
            shall have my music for nothing.

CALIBAN   When Prospero is destroyed.

            Another part of the island. The king and his
            followers are walking wearily through a wood.

GONZALO   By'r lakin, I can go no further, sir; my old
            bones ache.

ALONSO   Old lord, I cannot blame thee. Sit down
            and rest.

> *The king, Gonzalo and the attendant lords sit;*
> *Sebastian and Antonio draw apart.*

SEBASTIAN   (*touching his sword*) The next advantage will we take thoroughly.

ANTONIO   Let it be tonight.

> *A strange, solemn music fills the air.*

ANTONIO   What harmony is this?

GONZALO   Marvellous sweet music!

> *From concealment, Prospero watches his enemies. He raises his staff. Strange shapes, with beast and bird heads, appear, bearing a rich banquet. They set it down before the amazed company, bow, and vanish as suddenly as they had come.*

ALONSO   Give us kind keepers, heavens! What were these?

SEBASTIAN   A living drollery.

GONZALO   If in Naples I should report this now, would they believe me?

ALONSO   I cannot too much muse such shapes, such gesture, and such sound expressing (although they want the use of tongue) a kind of excellent dumb discourse.

PROSPERO   (*to the apparitions*) Praise in departing.

GONZALO   They vanished strangely.

SEBASTIAN   No matter, since they have left their viands behind. Will't please you taste of what is here?

As they advance towards the table, there is thunder and lightning. The air darkens, and with a thudding of leathery wings, Ariel, in the form of a harpy, a hideous bird with the head of a hag, flies down and perches on the table. Prospero's enemies look on in astonishment when, at a clap of the bird's wings, the banquet vanishes.

ARIEL   (*screaming*) You are three men of sin –

All draw their swords and advance upon the apparition.

ARIEL   You fools! I and my fellows are ministers of Fate. Your swords are now too massy for your strengths.

Swords fall from helpless hands. The king and his company are motionless, spellbound.

ARIEL   You three from Milan did supplant good
         Prospero: exposed unto the sea him and his
         innocent child; for which foul deed the powers,
         delaying, not forgetting, have incensed the
         seas and shores, yea, all the creatures, against
         your peace. Thee of thy son, Alonso, they
         have bereft; and do pronounce by me
         ling'ring perdition . . .

         Thunder and lightning; and Ariel vanishes.

ALONSO   O, it is monstrous, monstrous! Methought the
         billows spoke, and told me it, the winds did sing
         it to me, and the thunder, that deep and
         dreadful organ-pipe, pronounced the name
         of Prosper: therefore my son i'th'ooze is
         bedded; and I'll seek him deeper than e'er
         plummet sounded, and with him there
         lie mudded . . .

         *Before Prospero's cell, Ferdinand and Miranda
         together. Prospero smiles upon them. His harshness
         towards Ferdinand has vanished.*

PROSPERO If I have too austerely punished you, your
         compensation makes amends. All thy vexations
         were but my trials of thy love, and thou hast
         strangely stood the test. Here, afore heaven, I
         ratify this, my rich gift. (*He gives Ferdinand
         Miranda's willing hand.*)

378

FERDINAND   I do believe it, against an oracle.

PROSPERO   Then, as my gift, and thine own acquisition,
                 worthily purchased, take my daughter. Sit then
                 and talk with her, she is thine own.

                 *Prospero leaves the lovers to converse while he
                 moves aside.*

PROSPERO   What Ariel! my industrious servant, Ariel!

ARIEL   (*appearing*) What would my potent master?

PROSPERO   Go bring the rabble (o'er whom I give thee
                 power) here to this place. Incite them to quick
                 motion, for I must bestow upon the eyes of this
                 young couple some vanity of mine art. It is my
                 promise, and they expect it from me. (*Ariel
                 departs on Prospero's errand. Prospero returns to
                 Ferdinand and Miranda, who are embracing.
                 Prospero shakes his head warningly.*)

PROSPERO   Do not give dalliance too much the rein.

FERDINAND   (*guiltily freeing Miranda*) I warrant you, sir –

PROSPERO   – No tongue! all eyes! Be silent!

                 *Prospero raises his staff. Music plays and the air
                 grows strangely bright, and full of swirling shapes.*

Iris, goddess of the rainbow appears, and, bowing, ushers in two goddesses more: Ceres, goddess of the harvest, and Juno, the queen of heaven.

JUNO   Honour, riches, marriage-blessing,
                Long continuance and increasing,
                Hourly joys be still upon you,
                Juno sings her blessings on you.

CERES   Earth's increase, foison plenty,
                Barns and garners never empty,
                Scarcity and want shall shun you,
                Ceres' blessing so is on you.

FERDINAND   *(awed)* This is a most majestic vision! May I
                be bold to think these spirits?

PROSPERO   Spirits which, by mine art, I have from
                their confines called to enact my present
                fancies.

                More spirits appear, and dance gracefully.

FERDINAND   Let me live here ever! So rare a wondered father
                and a wise makes this place Paradise.

                Prospero smiles. Suddenly his brow darkens.

PROSPERO   I had forgot that foul conspiracy of Caliban and
                his confederates against my life. The minute of

their plot is almost come. Well done! Avoid!
No more!

*He gestures with his staff. The music jangles into
discord and the spirits that have presented the
marvellous vision fly, as if in terror. Ferdinand and
Miranda look frightened.*

PROSPERO   You do look, my son, in a moved sort, as if you
were dismayed; be cheerful, sir. Our revels now
are ended. These our actors (as I foretold you)
were all spirits, and are melted into air, into
thin air, and like the baseless fabric of this
vision, the cloud clapped towers, the gorgeous
palaces, the solemn temples, the great globe
itself, yea, all which it inherit, shall dissolve,
and like this insubstantial pageant faded leave
not a rack behind. We are such stuff as dreams
are made on; and our little life is rounded
with a sleep. Sir, I am vexed; bear with my
weakness. If you be pleased, retire into my
cell. A turn or two I'll walk to still my
beating mind.

The lovers retire into Prospero's cell.

PROSPERO   Ariel, come!

ARIEL   (*appearing*) What's thy pleasure?

PROSPERO   Spirit, we must prepare to meet with Caliban.
            Where didst thou leave these varlots?

ARIEL   They were red-hot with drinking, so full of
            valour that they smote the air for breathing in
            their faces! I left them i'th'filthy-mantled
            pool beyond your cell, there dancing up
            to th'chins, that the foul lake o'erstunk
            their feet!

PROSPERO   This was well done, my bird. The trumpery in
            my house, go bring it hither, for stale to catch
            these thieves! (*Ariel departs.*) I will plague them
            all, even to roaring.

            Ariel returns, bearing a host of rich garments,
            which, on Prospero's direction, are hung on a line
            close by the entrance to his cell. Then Prospero and
            Ariel conceal themselves. Even as they do so, the
            conspirators enter: Caliban, Stephano and Trinculo.
            They are soaked with filthy water.

CALIBAN   Pray you tread softly; we now are near
            his cell.

TRINCULO   Monster, I do smell all horse-piss, at which my
            nose is in great indignation.

STEPHANO   So is mine. Do you hear, monster?

382

CALIBAN   Prithee, my king, be quiet. Seest thou here, this
            is the mouth o'th'cell. No noise, and enter.

STEPHANO   Give me thy hand. I do begin to have
            bloody thoughts.

            Suddenly Trinculo sees the garments on the line.

TRINCULO   O King Stephano! Look what a wardrobe is
            here for thee!

            *At once, the two drunkards busy themselves with all
            the fine clothing.*

CALIBAN   Let it alone, thou fool, it is but trash!

STEPHANO   (*covetously*) Put off that gown, Trinculo. By this
            hand, I'll have that gown!

            He tears the coveted garment off Trinculo.

CALIBAN   Let it alone, and do the murder first!

STEPHANO   Monster, go to, carry this!

            He thrusts an armful of garments on Caliban.

TRINCULO   And this. (*More garments.*)

STEPHANO   Ay, and this!

Prospero raises his staff. At once, there is a sound of hunting horns, and out of the wood come huge, savage hounds, baying and barking. The would-be murderers howl in terror and dismay. They fly from the hounds. Prospero and Ariel urged the hunt on.

PROSPERO   Hey, Mountain, hey!

ARIEL   Silver! There goes Silver!

PROSPERO   Fury, Fury! There, Tyrant there! Hark, hark!

The sounds of barking and the howls of the pursued die away.

PROSPERO   Say, my spirit, how fares the King and's followers?

ARIEL   Just as you left them – all prisoners, sir. They cannot budge till your release. Your charm so strongly works 'em that if you now beheld them your affections would become tender.

PROSPERO   Dost think so, spirit?

ARIEL   Mine would, sir, were I human.

PROSPERO   And mine shall. The rarer action is in virtue than in vengeance. Go release them, Ariel.

*Ariel departs. Prospero draws a circle on the ground
with his staff. Sadly, he shakes his head.*

PROSPERO   This rough magic I here abjure; and when I have
required some heavenly music (which even now
I do) to work mine end upon their senses that
this airy charm is for, I'll break my staff, bury it
certain fathoms in the earth, and deeper than
did ever plummet sound I'll drown my book.

*There is solemn music; Ariel leads the spellbound
king and his followers into Prospero's magic circle,
and leaves them, stiff and doll-like. Prospero now
takes off his magic mantle and reveals the stately
dress of the Duke of Milan. He waves his staff.
The spell is lifted, and the prisoners blink
in amazement.*

PROSPERO   Behold, sir King, the wronged Duke of
Milan, Prospero.

Alonso falls to his knees.

ALONSO   Thy dukedom I resign, and do entreat thou
pardon me my wrongs. But how should
Prospero be living, and be here?

PROSPERO   (*to Gonzalo*) First, noble friend, let me
embrace thine age, whose honour cannot be
measured or confined.

GONZALO   Whether this be, or be not, I'll not swear.

PROSPERO   You do yet taste some subtleties o' the isle, that
            will not let you believe things certain. Welcome,
            my friends all! (*He turns to Sebastian and
            Antonio.*) But you, my brace of lords, were I so
            minded, I here could pluck his Highness' frown
            upon you and justify you traitors. At this time I
            will tell no tales.

SEBASTIAN   (*aside*) The devil speaks in him!

PROSPERO   No. For you, most wicked sir, whom to call
            brother would even infect my mouth, I do
            forgive thy rankest fault—all of them; and
            require my dukedom of thee, which perforce, I
            know thou must restore.

            *Antonio scowls and shrugs his shoulders. He turns
            away. Prospero addresses the king.*

PROSPERO   This cell's my court. Pray you, look in. My
            dukedom since you have given me again, I will
            requite you with as good a thing.

            *They approach the entrance to the cell. Prospero
            draws aside a curtain, and reveals Ferdinand and
            Miranda, playing chess.*

MIRANDA   Sweet lord, you play me false.

386

FERDINAND   No, my dearest love, I would not for the world.

MIRANDA   Yes, for a score of kingdoms you should
wrangle, and I would call it fair play –

The lovers, seeing they are observed, break off.
Ferdinand runs to kneel at his father's feet.

FERDINAND   Though the seas threaten, they are merciful. I
have cursed them without cause!

ALONSO   (*embracing him*) All the blessings of a glad father
compass thee about!

MIRANDA   O, wonder! How many goodly creatures are
there here! How beauteous mankind is! O brave
new world, that has such people in it!

PROSPERO   'Tis new to thee.

ALONSO   Who is this maid with whom thou wast at play?
Is she the goddess that hath severed us, and
brought us together?

FERDINAND   Sir, she is mortal; but by immortal Providence
she's mine. She is daughter to this famous Duke
of Milan.

The king warmly embraces his son and his
son's bride. Ariel enters, leading the ship's

387

master and the boatswain, both in a state of dreamlike wonderment.

GONZALO   O look sir, look sir, here is more of us! What is the news?

BOATSWAIN   The best news is that we have safely found our king and company; the next, our ship – which but three glasses since, we gave out split – is tight and yare and bravely rigged as when we first put out to sea!

ARIEL   (*aside to Prospero*) Was't well done?

PROSPERO   Bravely, my diligence. Thou shalt be free. (*Ariel soars into the air and disappears.*)

ALONSO   This is as strange a maze as e'er men trod –

PROSPERO   There are yet missing of your company some few odd lads that you remember not. (*Ariel returns, driving a woeful Caliban and the reeling, drunken, tattered Stephano and Trinculo.*) Two of these fellows you must know and own. This thing of darkness I acknowledge mine. (*He turns to Caliban.*) Go, sirrah, to my cell. As you look to have my pardon, trim it handsomely.

CALIBAN   Ay, that I will; and I'll be wise hereafter, and seek for grace. What a thrice double ass was I to take this drunkard for a god, and worship this dull fool!

The three would-be lords of the isle stumble away to nurse their bruises and ease their cramps.

ALONSO   I long to hear the story of your life, which must take the ear strangely.

PROSPERO   I'll deliver all, and promise you calm seas . . . (*To Ariel, aside*) My Ariel, chick, that is thy charge. Then to the elements be free, and fare thou well.

Prospero raises his hand in farewell. Then, with a courteous gesture, he conducts the company into his cell. For a moment, he remains alone. Then he breaks his magic staff and casts it away. Then he goes into the cell.

High up in the air, Ariel sings:

> Where the bee sucks, there suck I,
> In a cowslip's bell I lie;
> There I couch when owls do cry.
> On the bat's back I do fly
> After summer merrily.
> Merrily, merrily shall I live now,
> Under the blossom that hangs on the bough.

The curtain falls on the vessel that carries the king and his company back to Naples, and Prospero back to his dukedom, leaving Caliban to seek grace on the island.

Macbeth

This is one of the darkest of Shakespeare's plays, and perhaps the most terrifying play ever written. Set in ancient Scotland, it is a tale of witchcraft, murder and madness. It is the tale of a great soldier who is tempted by wicked prophecies into seizing the crown of Scotland by murdering the king.

Shakespeare wrote the play when he was about forty-two. He found the story in Ralph Holinshed's *Chronicles of England, Scotland and Ireland*, and altered it to suit his dramatic purposes. It is one of the shortest of the plays, and by far the most concentrated.

Macbeth himself dominates it; all others, even his 'fiend-like queen', pale beside his huge presence; and we watch, in horrified fascination, as he, with eyes wide open, and knowing all the consequences, chooses evil instead of good; for his creed is the most dangerous of all: 'for mine own good all causes shall give way.'

It is a play about evil; and evil rises from it like a poisoned fog, choking out all light. Black is its prevailing colour, relieved only by the red glare of blood. 'Who would have thought the old man to have had so much blood in him?' wonders Lady

Macbeth, walking in her hideous sleep, as she and her murderous husband go their divided ways to the 'everlasting bonfire'.

The Characters in the Play

in order of appearance

FIRST WITCH

SECOND WITCH

THIRD WITCH

DUNCAN · *King of Scotland*

MACBETH · *Thane of Glamis, later of Cawdor, later King of Scotland*

BANQUO
ROSSE · *Thanes of Scotland*
ANGUS

LADY MACBETH

SERVANT · *to Lady Macbeth*

MACDUFF
LENNOX · *Thanes of Scotland*

DONALBAIN
MALCOLM · *Sons to Duncan*

FLEANCE · *Banquo's son*

LORDS

MURDERER

FIRST APPARITION

SECOND APPARITION

THIRD APPARITION

DOCTOR

WOMAN · *attendant on Lady Macbeth*

FIRST NOBLE

SECOND NOBLE

COURTIER

SOLDIER

The curtain rises on a wild heath under a dark, ragged sky Thunder and lightning. Three hideous old women, huddled together, screaming with malignant laughter.

1ST WITCH	When shall we three meet again? In thunder, lightning, or in rain?
2ND WITCH	When the hurly-burly's done, when the battle's lost and won!
1ST WITCH	Where the place?
2ND WITCH	Upon the heath!
3RD WITCH	There to meet with Macbeth!

They stare at one another, and nod.

ALL   Fair is foul and foul is fair: hover through the fog and filthy air!

Thunder and lightning. The witches vanish.

The battle is for Scotland itself. Norway has invaded. In the midst of the mad confusion of battle, the gigantic figures of Macbeth and Banquo, his companion-in-arms, lay about them with ceaseless swords. They are the great generals of Duncan, lawful king of Scotland.

Presently the battle subsides. The survivors cheer and raise their swords and spears to Macbeth, the victor. He waves his sword in acknowledgement; and Banquo, taking up a drum from a fallen boy, rattles out a roll of triumph.

In the royal camp, good king Duncan learns with joy of Macbeth's victory; but at the same time, hears of the treachery of the Thane of Cawdor, who has been captured. Sadly, he shakes his head.

DUNCAN There's no art to find the mind's construction in the face. He was a gentleman on whom I built an absolute trust. Go pronounce his present death, and with his former title greet Macbeth. What he hath lost, noble Macbeth hath won.

The heath. Madman's weather! Macbeth and Banquo are on their way to the royal camp.

MACBETH So fair and foul a day I have not seen.

Suddenly they halt. Their way is barred by three hideous old women!

BANQUO What are these, withered and so wild in their attire?

They do not answer. Banquo thumps on his drum.

BANQUO　　Live you? Or are you aught that man may question?

One by one, the witches raise their skinny fingers to their lips. They gaze at Macbeth.

MACBETH　　Speak if you can! What are you?

1ST WITCH　　All hail, Macbeth, hail to thee, Thane of Glamis!

Banquo thumps in agreement.

2ND WITCH　　All hail, Macbeth, hail to thee, Thane of Cawdor!

Banquo, drumsticks raised, hesitates.

3RD WITCH　　All hail, Macbeth, that shalt be king hereafter!

The drumsticks fall. Macbeth bends to pick them up.

BANQUO　　If you can look into the seeds of time and say which grain will grow, and which will not, speak then to me.

Macbeth

1ST WITCH   Lesser than Macbeth and greater.

2ND WITCH   Not so happy, yet much happier.

3RD WITCH   Thou shalt get kings though thou be none!

*With each pronouncement, Macbeth taps
humorously on Banquo's drum; but with the
last, his blow is violent and splits the
drumskin. The rent is in the form of a dagger!
Macbeth and Banquo stare at it. As they do
so, the witches vanish.*

BANQUO.   The earth hath bubbles, as the water has,
and these are of them –

MACBETH   Your children shall be kings.

BANQUO   You shall be king –

MACBETH   – And Thane of Cawdor too; went it
not so?

*As they stare into the terrible air, two ghostly
figures appear. As they draw near, they are
seen to be two messengers from the king: Rosse
and Angus. They salute Macbeth.*

ROSSE   The king hath happily received,
Macbeth, the news of thy kingdom's

great success. Everyone did bear thy
praises, in his kingdom's great defence,
and poured them down before him. He
bade me, from him, call thee Thane
of Cawdor!

BANQUO   (*aside*) What! Can the Devil speak true?

MACBETH   The Thane of Cawdor lives; why do you
              dress me in borrowed robes?

ANGUS   Who was the Thane lives yet; but under
              heavy judgement bears that life which he
              deserves to lose.

Macbeth, in high excitement, turns aside.

MACBETH   Glamis, and Thane of Cawdor! Two truths
              are told, as happy prologues to the swelling
              act of the imperial theme! Stars, hide
              your fires! Let not light see my black and
              deep desires!

*At Inverness, in the castle of Macbeth, his wife
reads a letter from her husband. It tells of the
meeting with the weird sisters and their
marvellous prophecies, one of which has
already come true. She puts aside the letter and
paces the room.*

LADY MACBETH Glamis thou art, and Cawdor, and shalt be
what thou art promised. – Yet do I fear thy
nature; it is too full of the milk of human
kindness, to catch the nearest way. Thou
wouldst be great, art not without ambition,
but without the illness should attend it. Hie
thee hither that I may pour my spirits in
thine ear –

*Comes a knocking on the door. A
servant enters.*

LADY MACBETH What's your tidings?

SERVANT The King comes here tonight –

LADY MACBETH Thou'rt mad to say it!

SERVANT So please you, it is true.

*She dismisses the servant. She is alone. The
harsh cry of a raven causes her to start. Her
eyes blaze with a terrible desire.*

LADY MACBETH The raven himself is hoarse that croaks the
fatal entrance of Duncan under my
battlements! Come, you spirits that tend
on mortal thoughts, unsex me here, and fill
me, from the crown to the toe, top-full of
direst cruelty! Come to my woman's

399

breasts, and take my milk for gall, you murdering ministers –

The door bursts open. Macbeth, still blood-stained from battle, stands before her.

LADY MACBETH Great Glamis, worthy Cawdor, greater than both by the all-hail hereafter!

MACBETH My dearest love, Duncan comes here tonight.

LADY MACBETH And when goes hence?

MACBETH Tomorrow, as he purposes.

LADY MACBETH O never shall sun that morrow see! Your face, my thane, is as a book where men may read strange matters. To beguile the time look like the time, bear welcome in your eye, your hand, your tongue; look like the innocent flower, but be the serpent under't. He that's coming must be provided for; and you shall put this night's great business into my dispatch, which shall to all our nights and days to come give solely sovereign sway and masterdom.

MACBETH (*uncertainly*) We will speak further –

LADY MACBETH   Only look up clear; leave all the rest to me.

The courtyard of the castle. King Duncan, accompanied by his sons, Malcolm and Donalbain, and a train of nobles and servants, has arrived. Lady Macbeth greets him with loyal smiles and humble curtsies.

DUNCAN   Conduct me to mine host; we love him highly.

Evening. A banquet is in progress to honour the royal guest. The door of the dinning-chamber opens briefly and a dark figure emerges. It is Macbeth. He is deeply disturbed.

MACBETH   If it were done, when 'tis done, then 'twere well it were done quickly: if the assassination could trammel up the consequence . . .? He's here in double trust; first as I am his kinsman and his subject, strong both against the deed; then as his host who should against his murderer shut the door, not bear the knife myself. Besides, this Duncan hath borne his faculties so meek, hath been so clear in his great office, that his virtues will plead like angels, trumpet-tongued, against the deep damnation of his taking-off –

The door opens and closes again. Lady Macbeth has followed him, leaving King Duncan at the banquet table.

LADY MACBETH   Why have you left the chamber?

MACBETH   We will proceed no further in this business.

LADY MACBETH   Art thou afeard to be the same in thine own act and valour as thou art in desire?

MACBETH   Prithee, peace! I dare do all that may become a man, who dares do more is none.

LADY MACBETH   What beast was't then that made you break this enterprise to me?

MACBETH   If we should fail?

LADY MACBETH   We fail? But screw your courage to the sticking-place and we'll not fail!

Night. The great hall of the castle. All is quiet. A flickering light appears. Macbeth, with a servant, bearing a torch. They halt.

MACBETH   Go bid thy mistress, when my drink is ready, she strike upon the bell.

The servant departs, leaving the torch to glimmer on the spears and shields that hang upon the wall. Its light, reflected on the polished surfaces, seems to form the shapes of daggers . . .

MACBETH
Is this a dagger which I see before me, the handle toward my hand? . . . or art thou but a dagger of the mind . . .?

Faintly, there is the sound of a bell. Macbeth draws in his breath sharply.

MACBETH
I go, and it is done: the bell invites me. Hear it not, Duncan, for it is a knell that summons thee to Heaven, or to Hell.

Silently, he leaves the hall and begins to mount a stairway . . . In the hall below, a softly gliding shadow appears. It is Lady Macbeth. An owl cries.

LADY MACBETH
Hark! Peace! It was the owl that shrieked. (*She looks up toward the stairway, where Macbeth has vanished.*) He is about it: the doors are open, and the surfeited grooms do mock their charge with snores. I have drugged their possets . . . Had he not resembled my father as he slept, I had done it.

403

*There is a slight noise. Macbeth descends
the stairs.*

MACBETH   I have done the deed.

LADY MACBETH   My husband!

MACBETH   (*staring at his bloody hands*) This is a
                   sorry sight.

LADY MACBETH   A foolish thought, to say a sorry sight.
                   Why did you bring these daggers from
                   the place? They must lie there; go carry
                   them, and smear the sleepy grooms
                   with blood.

MACBETH   I'll go no more. I am afraid to think what I
                   have done; look on't again I dare not.

LADY MACBETH   Give me the daggers! The sleeping and the
                   dead are but as pictures. 'Tis the eye of
                   childhood that fears a painted devil. If he
                   do bleed, I'll gild the faces of the grooms
                   withal, for it must seem their guilt!

                   *She snatches the daggers and hastens away.
                   Macbeth continues to stare at his hands.
                   Suddenly there is a loud knocking on the
                   castle's outer door.*

MACBETH   Whence is that knocking? How is't with me, when every noise appals me? Will all great Neptune's ocean wash this blood clean from my hand? No, this my hand will rather the multitudinous seas incarnadine, making the green one red!

Lady Macbeth returns. She holds up her hands. They are red.

LADY MACBETH   My hands are of your colour, but I shame to wear a heart so white.

Again, the knocking.

LADY MACBETH   Retire we to our chamber. A little water clears us of this deed. Get on your nightgown . . . Be not lost so poorly in your thoughts!

MACBETH   To know my deed, 'twere best not know myself.

For a third time, comes the knocking.

MACBETH   Wake Duncan with thy knocking: I would thou couldst!

The great door of the castle is opened. Macduff, the mighty Thane of Fife, with

Lennox, a nobleman, have come to awaken the king. Macbeth, scrambled into night-attire, greets him.

MACDUFF   Is the King stirring, worthy Thane?

MACBETH   Not yet.

MACDUFF   He did bid me to call timely upon him.

MACBETH   I'll bring you to him.

He indicates the king's chamber and stands aside.

LENNOX   Goes the King hence today?

MACBETH   He does: he did appoint so.

LENNOX   The night has been unruly. Where we lay, our chimneys were blown down, and, as they say, lamentings heard i'the air; strange screams of death . . .

Macduff rushes out of the king's chamber.

MACDUFF   Horror, horror, horror! Awake, awake! Ring the alarum bell! Murder and treason!

*Uproar and terror in the castle! Banquo, the
king's sons and Lady Macbeth appear, white-
faced, amazed. Macbeth rushes into the king's
chamber.*

LADY MACBETH   What's the business?

MACDUFF   Our royal master's murdered!

LADY MACBETH   Woe, alas! What! In our house?

*Macbeth reappears. Malcolm and Donalbain,
still tousled with sleep, enter.*

DONALBAIN   What's amiss?

MACBETH   You are, and do not know it! The spring,
the head, the fountain of your blood
is stopped –

MACDUFF   Your royal father's murdered!

MALCOLM   O, by whom?

LENNOX   Those of his chamber, as it seemed, had
done't. Their hands and faces were all
badg'd with blood, so were their daggers –

MACBETH   O! yet do I repent me of my fury that I did
kill them!

407

MACDUFF   Wherefore did you so?

*All stare at Macbeth. Malcolm and Donalbain
draw apart. They whisper fearfully.*

MALCOLM   What will you do? I'll to England.

DONALBAIN   To Ireland, I. Our separated fortunes shall
keep us both the safer; where we are,
there's daggers in men's smiles; the near in
blood, the nearer bloody.

*Without a word, they vanish away like thieves
in the night, leaving behind Macbeth, and
the crown.*

*The crown of Scotland. In the great abbey
church at Scone, the golden round, held in the
trembling hands of a bishop, descends upon the
head of Macbeth. Beside him kneels his queen.
She is well satisfied. The second prophecy has
been fulfilled. Yet her husband's face, far from
triumphant, is bleak and haunted. He peers
uneasily at the faces of the attending nobles.
One, in particular, catches his eye. It
is Banquo.*

BANQUO   (*to himself*) Thou hast it now: King,
Cawdor, Glamis, all, as the weird women
promised, and I fear thou played'st most

foully for it; yet it was said it should not
stand in thy posterity, but that myself
should be the root and father of
many kings . . .

*A room in the royal palace. There is to be a
great feast to celebrate the crowning of
Macbeth. All the great ones of Scotland have
been hidden to attend. Among them is Banquo,
and Fleance, his son. Macbeth smiles fondly
at them.*

MACBETH   Tonight we hold a solemn supper, sir, and
               I'll request your presence.

BANQUO   Let your highness command upon me.

MACBETH   Ride you this afternoon?

BANQUO   Ay, my good lord.

MACBETH   Is't far you ride?

BANQUO   As far, my lord, as will fill up the time
               'twixt this and supper.

MACBETH   Goes Fleance with you?

BANQUO   Ay, my good lord.

MACBETH   Fail not our feast.

BANQUO   My lord, I will not.

               Banquo and his son depart. Macbeth is alone.
               He goes to a window and stares out over the
               palace gardens.

MACBETH   To be thus is nothing, but to be safely thus.
               Our fears in Banquo stick deep . . .

               He raises his hand. Below, two grim figures
               emerge from the concealment of bushes. They
               look up. Macbeth nods. They salute, and
               vanish. The door opens. Lady Macbeth enters
               and goes over to Macbeth.

LADY MACBETH   How now, my lord, why do you keep alone?
               Things without all remedy should be
               without regard; what's done is done.

MACBETH   We have scorched the snake, not killed it;
               she'll close and be herself . . . Better be with
               the dead, whom we, to gain our peace, have
               sent to peace. Duncan is in his grave; after
               life's fitful fever he sleeps well . . .

LADY MACBETH   You must leave this!

MACBETH   O! full of scorpions is my mind, dear wife!

Thou knowest that Banquo and his
Fleance lives.

LADY MACBETH   What's to be done?

MACBETH   Be innocent of the knowledge, dearest
chuck, till thou applaud the deed. Come,
seeling night, scarf up the tender eye of
pitiful day, and with thy bloody and
invisible hand cancel and tear to pieces that
great bond which keeps me pale! Light
thickens, and the crow makes wing to the
rooky wood; good things of day begin to
droop and drowse, whiles night's black
agents to their prey do rouse. Thou
marvel'st at my words, but hold thee still:
things bad begun make strong themselves
by ill.

*The banqueting chamber. The flower of
Scotland's nobility buzz and jostle in
blossoming profusion. Sliding among them,
serpent-like, Lady Macbeth darts her head
from side to side, tasting the sweet air
of royalty.*

LADY MACBETH   You know your own degrees, sit down . . .

LORDS   Thanks to your Majesty!

They seat themselves at the great table. Music begins to play: the wild wailing of bagpipes and the rattle of a drum. A shadow lurks by the door: a muffled figure, beckoning. Macbeth observes it, and quietly approaches. The figure draws aside the covering of its face.

MACBETH   There's blood upon thy face.

MURDERER   'Tis Banquo's then.

MACBETH   Is he dispatched?

MURDERER   My lord, his throat is cut.

MACBETH   Thou art the best o' the cut-throats, yet he's good that did the like for Fleance!

MURDERER   Most royal sir, Fleance is scaped.

MACBETH   Then comes my fit again! I had else been perfect, but now I am cabined, cribbed, confined. But Banquo's safe?

MURDERER   Ay, my good lord; safe in a ditch he bides, with twenty trenched gashes on his head.

MACBETH   Thanks for that. Get thee gone.

The murderer, with a soldierly salute, vanishes away. Macbeth returns to his guests. He stares, puzzled, at the table.

LENNOX   May't please your highness, sit.

MACBETH   The table's full.

LENNOX   Here is a place reserved, sir.

MACBETH   Where?

LENNOX   Here, my good lord.

He gestures. Macbeth stares. In the offered place sits the ghost of Banquo!

MACBETH   Which of you have done this?

LORDS   What, my good lord?

The apparition raises its hand and points at Macbeth. Macbeth staggers in horror.

MACBETH   Thou canst not say I did it! Never shake thy gory locks at me!

Bewilderment at the table.

ROSSE   Gentlemen, rise, his highness is not well!

LADY MACBETH   Sit, worthy friends, my lord is often thus!
                Pray you keep seat! (*She goes to her
                husband's side, grasps him by the arm, and
                whispers fiercely*) Are you a man? This is the
                very painting of your fear! Why do you
                make such faces? When all's done, you look
                but on a stool!

MACBETH   (*pointing at the apparition*) Prithee, see
                there! The time has been, that when the
                brains were out, the man would die, and
                there an end; but now they rise again, with
                twenty mortal murders on their crowns,
                and push us from our stools.

                *The ghost vanishes. Macbeth makes an effort
                to recover himself. He takes up a glass of wine,
                and offers a toast.*

MACBETH   Come, love and health to all! And to our
                dear friend Banquo, whom we miss! Would
                he were here!

                *He makes as if to drink. The music plays
                loudly; in particular, the drum. He glances at
                the drummer. It is Banquo! He hurls his glass
                at the ghost.*

MACBETH   Avaunt, and quit my sight! Thy bones are
                marrowless, thy blood is cold; thou hast no

speculation in those eyes which thou dost glare with! Hence, horrible shadow! Unreal mockery, hence!

A clatter of falling stools as everyone rises in alarm and amazement. A hubbub of voices, wondering what's amiss.

LADY MACBETH   I pray you, speak not! He grows worse and worse, question enrages him – at once, good night! Stand not upon the order of your going, but go at once!

Confusedly, the guests depart. Presently Macbeth and his wife are alone, amid the ruins of the feast.

MACBETH   It will have blood, they say: blood will have blood. What is the night?

LADY MACBETH   Almost at odds with morning, which is which.

MACBETH   How say'st thou, that Macduff denies his person at our great bidding?

LADY MACBETH   Did you send to him, sir?

MACBETH   I heard it by the way; but I will send. There's not a one of them but in his house

I keep a servant fee'd. I will tomorrow to
the weird sisters. More shall they speak; for
I am bent to know by the worst means, the
worst. I am in blood stepped in so far, that
should I wade no more, returning were as
tedious as going o'er.

LADY MACBETH   You lack the season of all natures, sleep.

MACBETH   Come, we'll to sleep. We are yet but young
in deed.

*Within a mean and smoky house, the three
witches move slowly about a black cauldron
that hisses and spits above a fire. As they
revolve, they cast their strange offerings into the
boiling pot.*

1ST WITCH   Round about the cauldron go, in the
poisoned entrails throw; toad that
under cold stone days and nights has
thirty-one.

ALL   Double, double, toil and trouble; fire burn
and cauldron bubble.

2ND WITCH   Fillet of a fenny snake, in the cauldron boil
and bake. Eye of newt and toe of frog, wool
of bat and tongue of dog . . .

ALL   Double, double, toil and trouble; fire burn and cauldron bubble.

3RD WITCH   Finger of birth-strangled babe ditch-delivered by a drab, make the gruel thick and slab . . .

ALL   Double, double, toil and trouble; fire burn and cauldron bubble . . .

Comes a knocking on the door.

2ND WITCH   By the pricking of my thumbs, something wicked this way comes! Open, locks, whoever knocks!

The door opens. Macbeth enters. Vanished is the once noble warrior. His face is savage and depraved.

MACBETH   How now, you secret, black, and midnight hags? What is't you do?

ALL   A deed without a name.

MACBETH   Answer me to what I ask you.

1ST WITCH   Speak.

2ND WITCH   Demand.

3RD WITCH	We'll answer.
1ST WITCH	Say if th'hadst rather hear it from our mouths, or from our masters?
MACBETH	Call 'em; let me see 'em.

They nod. Then, from a homely jug, one of them pours blood into the cauldron. It spits in a fury. Dense vapours arise and out of the swirling air, a strange sight appears, to the accompaniment of thunder. It is a helmeted head.

1ST APPARITION	Macbeth, Macbeth, Macbeth, beware Macduff, beware the Thane of Fife.

The apparition vanishes. Macbeth nods grimly.

MACBETH	Thou hast harped my fear aright. But –

Thunder again. A second apparition. It is a bloody child.

2ND APPARITION	Macbeth, Macbeth, Macbeth, be bloody, bold and resolute. None of woman born shall harm Macbeth.
MACBETH	Then live Macduff – what need I fear of

thee? But yet I'll make assurance double sure . . . thou shalt not live!

The second apparition dissolves away, and gives way, with a further, solemn roll of thunder, to a third apparition. It is a crowned child with a branch in its hand.

3RD APPARITION   Macbeth shall never vanquished be until great Birnam Wood to high Dunsinane Hill shall come against him. (*It vanishes.*)

MACBETH   That will never be. Who can impress the forest, bid the tree unfix his earth-bound root? Yet my heart throbs to know one thing: shall Banquo's issue ever reign in this kingdom?

ALL   Seek to know no more.

MACBETH   I will be satisfied!

Strange music. The fire dies, the cauldron sinks into the earth.

ALL   Show his eyes, and grieve his heart; come like shadows, so depart.

Out of the thick air stalks a procession of crowned kings. There are eight of them. Last of all comes murdered, bloody Banquo. Banquo points to the kings, then to himself, and smiles. The vision and the witches disappear. Macbeth is alone.

MACBETH   Where are they? Gone? Let this pernicious hour stand aye accursed in the calendar! (*There's a knocking on the door*) Come in, without there!

Lennox enters.

MACBETH   Saw you the weird sisters?

LENNOX   No, my lord.

MACBETH   Came they not by you?

LENNOX   No indeed, my lord.

MACBETH   Infected be the air whereon they ride, and damned all those that trust them! I did hear the galloping of horse. Who was't came by?

LENNOX   'Tis two or three, my lord, that bring you word Macduff is fled to England.

MACBETH   Time, thou anticipat'st my exploits! From this moment the very firstlings of my heart

420

shall be the firstlings of my hand! The
castle of Macduff I will surprise, seize upon
Fife, give to the edge of the sword his wife,
his babes, and all unfortunate souls that
trace him in his line. No boasting like a
fool; this deed I'll do before this
purpose cool.

*A room in the palace. Macbeth gazes out of his
murderer's window, across a wide landscape,
towards a distant castle on an eminence. He
raises his hand. Tiny black figures, like
malignant beetles, scurry across the green land
and mount the hillside towards the castle. They
reach it and swarm up its walls, finding little
entrances and penetrating them. On the
battlements they reappear, hurling white-
gowned figures to their deaths. Tiny screams
reach the watcher at the window, who nods . . .*

*A sunlit field in peaceful England. Malcolm
and Macduff stand together.*

MACDUFF   Not in the legions of horrid Hell can
              come a devil more damned in evils to
              top Macbeth.

MALCOLM   Our poor country sinks beneath the yoke.
              Here from gracious England have I offer of
              goodly thousands . . .

As they talk, a horseman approaches, weary and travel-stained. It is Rosse.

MALCOLM   My ever gentle cousin, welcome hither. Stands Scotland where it did?

ROSSE   Alas, poor country! The dead man's knell is there scarce asked for who, and good men's lives expire before the flowers in their caps.

MALCOLM   What's the newest grief?

MACDUFF   How does my wife?

ROSSE   Why, well.

MACDUFF   And all my children?

ROSSE   They were well at peace when I did leave 'em.

MACDUFF   Be not a niggard of your speech. Keep it not from me; quickly, let me have it.

ROSSE   Your castle is surprised; your wife and babes savagely slaughtered –

MALCOLM   Merciful Heaven!

MACDUFF   My children too?

ROSSE   Wife, children, servants, all that could
         be found.

MACDUFF My wife killed too?

ROSSE   I have said.

MACDUFF He has no children! Did you say all? – O
         Hell-kite! – All? What, all my pretty
         chickens and their dam at one
         fell swoop?

MALCOLM Let grief convert to anger –

MACDUFF Front to front bring you this fiend of
         Scotland and myself; within my sword's
         length set him!

MALCOLM Our power is ready. Macbeth is ripe
         for shaking . . .

         *The high dark castle of Dunsinane. It is
         night. In a quiet ante-chamber, a doctor and
         a waiting-gentlewoman stand and
         murmur together.*

DOCTOR   I have two nights watched with you, but
         can perceive no truth in your report. When
         was it –

> *Even as he speaks, a flickering light*
> *approaches. It is a taper, carried by Lady*
> *Macbeth. She is in her nightgown. As she*
> *walks, she rubs her hands together, causing the*
> *taper to tilt and cast wild shadows.*

WOMAN   Lo you, here she comes! This is her very
           guise, and upon my life, fast asleep.

DOCTOR   You see her eyes are open.

WOMAN   Ay, but their sense are shut.

DOCTOR   What is it she does now?

WOMAN   It is an accustomed action with her, to seem
           thus washing her hands: I have known her
           continue in this for a quarter of an hour.

LADY MACBETH   Look, here's a spot.

DOCTOR   Hark, she speaks.

LADY MACBETH   Out, damned spot! out, I say! – One; two:
           why, 'tis time to do't. – Fie, my lord, fie! a
           soldier, and afeard? – What need we fear
           who knows it, when none can call our
           power to accompt? – Yet who would have
           thought the old man to have had so much
           blood in him?

424

DOCTOR	Do you mark that?
LADY MACBETH	The Thane of Fife had a wife: where is she now? – What, will these hands ne'er be clean?
DOCTOR	Go to, go to, you have known what you should not!
WOMAN	She has spoke what she should not: I am sure of that; Heaven knows what she has known!
LADY MACBETH	Here's the smell of the blood still. All the perfumes of Arabia will not sweeten this little hand. O, O, O!
DOCTOR	What a sigh is there! The heart is sorely charged.
WOMAN	I would not have such a heart in my bosom for the dignity of the whole body.
DOCTOR	This disease is beyond my practice –
LADY MACBETH	Wash your hands, put on your nightgown; look not so pale. I tell you yet again, Banquo's buried: he cannot come out on's grave.

DOCTOR   Even so?

LADY MACBETH   To bed, to bed: there's knocking at the
                gate. Come, come, come, come, give me
                your hand. What's done cannot be undone.
                To bed, to bed, to bed . . .

                She drifts away.

DOCTOR   More needs she the divine than the
                physician. God, God forgive us all!

                *Open country, near Dunsinane. Two Scottish
                nobles on horse-back meet and exchange news.*

1ST NOBLE   The English power is near, led on by
                Malcolm and the good Macduff.

2ND NOBLE   Near Birnam Wood we shall meet them.

1ST NOBLE   What does the tyrant?

2ND NOBLE   Great Dunsinane he strongly fortifies.
                Some say he's mad . . .

1ST NOBLE   Now does he feel his secret murders sticking
                on his hands. Those he commands move
                only in command, nothing in love. Now
                does he feel his title hang loose about him,
                like a giant's robe upon a dwarfish thief.

Dunsinane castle. In a fierce and warlike chamber, hung with swords and spears and shields, Macbeth, watched by the doctor and attendants, paces to and fro in furious agitation. A servant enters, trembling.

MACBETH   The devil damn thee black, thou cream-faced loon! Where got'st thou that goose-look?

SERVANT   There is ten thousand –

MACBETH   – Geese, villain?

SERVANT   Soldiers, sir. The English force –

MACBETH   – Take thy face hence! (*The servant, trembling, departs.*)

MACBETH   I am sick at heart. I have lived long enough: my way of life is fallen into the sere, the yellow leaf, and that which should accompany old age, as honour, love, obedience, troops of friends, I must not look to have; but in their stead, curses, not loud but deep, mouth-honour . . . (*He turns to the doctor.*) How does your patient, doctor?

DOCTOR   Not so sick, my lord, as she is troubled

with thick-coming fancies, that keep her
from her rest.

MACBETH   Cure her of that: canst thou not minister to
a mind diseased, pluck from the memory a
rooted sorrow, raze out the written troubles
of the brain, and with some sweet oblivious
antidote cleanse the stuffed bosom of that
perilous stuff which weighs upon the heart?

DOCTOR   Therein the patient must minister
to himself.

MACBETH   Throw physic to the dogs; I'll none of it!
(*He turns to his attendants.*) Come, put
mine armour on! I'll fight till from my
bones my flesh be hacked! Till Birnam
Wood remove to Dunsinane, I cannot taint
with fear!

The English force, led by Malcolm and
Macduff, and a company of Scottish nobles.
Before them stands a forest . . .

NOBLE   What wood is this before us?

2ND NOBLE   The Wood of Birnam.

MALCOLM   Let every soldier hew him down a bough,
and bear it before him.

The order is passed. The soldiers advance and, with swords and axes, cripple the trees, leaving white wounds, like dead men's faces. Presently, another forest, it seems, begins to move across the land . . .

The courtyard of Dunsinane castle. A warlike scene. Macbeth in armour, with soldiers about him. Banners fly, drums roll.

MACBETH   Hang out our banners on the outward walls!

There is a sudden cry of women from high up in the castle.

MACBETH   What is that noise?

COURTIER   It is the cry of women, my good lord. (*He goes to discover the cause.*)

MACBETH   I have almost forgot the taste of fears: the time has been, my senses would have cooled to hear a night-shriek, and my fell of hair would at a dismal treatise rise and stir as life were in it. I have supped full with horrors . . .

The courtier returns. His face is grave.

MACBETH	Wherefore was that cry?
COURTIER	The Queen, my lord, is dead.
MACBETH	She should have died hereafter; there would have been a time for such a word. Tomorrow, and tomorrow, and tomorrow creeps in this petty pace from day to day, to the last syllable of recorded time: and all our yesterdays have lighted fools the way to dusty death. Out, out brief candle! Life's but a walking shadow, a poor player that struts and frets his hour upon this stage, and then is heard no more. It is a tale told by an idiot, full of sound and fury, signifying nothing.

A soldier approaches, staring-eyed.

MACBETH	Thou com'st to use thy tongue; thy story quickly!
SOLDIER	As I did stand my watch upon the hill, I looked toward Birnam, and anon methought the wood began to move!
MACBETH	Liar and slave!
SOLDIER	Within this three mile you may see it coming; I say, a moving grove!

MACBETH   If thou speak'st false . . . (*The man shakes his head violently. Macbeth dismisses him.*) I begin to doubt the equivocation of the fiend that lies like truth. 'Fear not till Birnam Wood do come to Dunsinane,' and now a wood comes towards Dunsinane. Arm, arm, and out! If this which he avouches does appear, there is no flying hence or tarrying here. I gin to be a-weary of the sun, and wish the estate of the world were now undone. Ring the alarum bell! Blow, wind! come wrack, at least we'll die with harness on our back!

He draws his sword and, with a shout of defiance, rushes from the castle, leading his soldiers down to the forest of trees that moves inexorably towards him.

The hillside. With furious shouts, the army of Macbeth rushes down towards the ever-oncoming wood. Suddenly, the leafy boughs are flung aside, and the forces of Malcolm and Macduff are revealed. In moments, the battle is engaged. The air is full of shrieks and shouts and bitter steel, and whirling dust. Macbeth in the midst, playing his trade of war with a giant's arm and strength.

431

MACBETH   They have tied me to the stake; I cannot
                 fly, but bear-like I must fight the course.

                 *A warrior confronts him. They fight. The
                 warrior is slain.*

MACBETH   What's he that was not born of woman?
                 Such a one am I to fear, or none!

                 *On another part of the hill, Macduff seeks
                 Macbeth.*

MACDUFF   That way the noise is. Tyrant, show thy face. If
                 thou be'st slain, and with no stroke of mine,
                 my wife and children's ghosts will haunt me
                 still. I cannot strike at wretched kerns, whose
                 arms are hired to bear their staves. Either
                 thou, Macbeth, or else my sword with an
                 unbattered edge I sheathe again undeeded.
                 There thou shouldst be: by this great clatter
                 one of greatest note seems bruited. Let me
                 find him, fortune! and more I beg not.

                 He sees Macbeth.

MACDUFF   Turn, hell-hound, turn!

MACBETH   (*turning*) Of all men else I have avoided
                 thee. But get thee back! My soul is too
                 much charged with blood of thine already!

MACDUFF   I have no words; my voice is my sword,
            thou bloodier villain than terms can give
            thee out.

            They fight.

MACBETH   Thou losest labour. I bear a charmed life,
            which must not yield to one of woman born!

MACDUFF   Despair thy charm, and let the Angel
            whom thou still hast served, tell thee,
            Macduff was from his mother's womb
            untimely ripped!

MACBETH   Accursed be that tongue that tells me so,
            for it hath cowed my better part of man!
            And be these juggling fiends no more
            believed, that palter with us in a double
            sense, that keep the word of promise to our
            ear, and break it to our hope. I'll not fight
            with thee.

MACDUFF   Then yield thee, coward; and live to be the
            show and gaze o'the time. We'll have thee,
            as our rarer monsters are, painted upon a
            pole, and underwrit, 'Here may you see
            the tyrant.'

MACBETH   I will not yield. Though Birnam Wood be
            come to Dunsinane, and thou opposed,

being of no woman born, yet will I try the last! Before my body I throw my warlike shield: lay on, Macduff, and damned be him that first cries, 'Hold, enough!'

They fight, and vanish into the clouds of dust, fighting. Suddenly there is a cry of dismay. The air thins and the head of Macbeth rises up, fierce and unrepentant. But the head is all. It has been severed at the neck, and is fixed upon the sword of Macduff.

There is a mighty shout of joy. Macbeth is dead: the battle has been lost and won.

The curtain falls . . .

William Shakespeare

Next to God, a wise man once said, Shakespeare created most. In the thirty-seven plays that are his chief legacy to the world – and surely no-one ever left a richer! – human nature is displayed in all its astonishing variety.

He has enriched the stage with matchless comedies, tragedies, histories, and, towards the end of his life, with plays

435

that defy all description, strange plays that haunt the imagination like visions.

His range is enormous: kings and queens, priests, princes and merchants, soldiers, clowns and drunkards, murderers, pimps, whores, fairies, monsters and pale, avenging ghosts 'strut and fret their hour upon the stage'. Murders and suicides abound; swords flash, blood flows, poison drips, and lovers sigh; yet there is always time for old men to talk of growing apples and for gardeners to discuss the weather.

In the four hundred years since they were written, they have become known and loved in every land; they are no longer the property of one country and one people, they are the priceless possession of the world.

His life, from what we know of it, was not astonishing. The stories that have attached themselves to him are remarkable only for their ordinariness: poaching deer, sleeping off a drinking bout under a wayside tree. There are no duels, no loud, passionate loves, no excesses of any kind. He was not one of your unruly geniuses whose habits are more interesting than their works. From all accounts, he was of a gentle, honourable disposition, a good businessman, and a careful father.

He was born on April 23rd 1564, to John and Mary Shakespeare of Henley Street, Stratford-upon-Avon. He was their third child and first son. When he was four or five he began his education at the local petty school. He left the local grammar school when he was about fourteen, in all probability to help in his father's glove-making shop. When he was eighteen, he married Anne Hathaway, who lived in a nearby village. By the time he was twenty-one, he was the father of three children, two daughters and a son.

A CATALOGVE

of the seuerall Comedies, Histories, and Tragedies contained in this Volume.

COMEDIES.

He Tempest.	Folio 1.
The two Gentlemen of Verona.	20
The Merry Wiues of Windsor.	38
Measure for Measure.	61
The Comedy of Errours.	85
Much adoo about Nothing.	101
Loues Labour lost.	122
Midsommer Nights Dreame.	145
The Merchant of Venice.	163
As you Like it.	185
The Taming of the Shrew.	208
All is well, that Ends well.	230
Twelfe-Night, or what you will.	255
The Winters Tale.	304

HISTORIES.

The Life and Death of King Iohn.	Fol. 1.
The Life & death of Richard the second.	23
The First part of King Henry the fourth.	46
The Second part of K. Henry the fourth.	74
The Life of King Henry the Fift.	69
The First part of King Henry the Sixt.	96
The Second part of King Hen. the Sixt.	120
The Third part of King Henry the Sixt.	147
The Life & Death of Richard the Third.	173
The Life of King Henry the Eight.	205

TRAGEDIES.

The Tragedy of Coriolanus.	Fol. 1.
Titus Andronicus.	31
Romeo and Juliet.	53
Timon of Athens.	80
The Life and death of Julius Cæsar.	109
The Tragedy of Macbeth.	131
The Tragedy of Hamlet.	152
King Lear.	283
Othello, the Moore of Venice.	310
Anthony and Cleopater.	346
Cymbeline King of Britaine.	369

Then, it seems, a restless mood came upon him. Maybe he travelled, maybe he was, as some say, a schoolmaster in the country; but at some time during the next seven years, he went to London and found employment in the theatre. When he was twenty-eight, he was already well enough known as an actor and playwright to excite the spiteful envy of a rival, who referred to him as 'an upstart crow'.

He mostly lived and worked in London until his mid-forties, when he returned to his family and home in Stratford, where he remained in prosperous circumstances until his death on April 23rd 1616, his fifty-second birthday.

He left behind him a widow, two daughters (his son died in childhood), and the richest imaginary world ever created by the human mind.

LEON GARFIELD

The list of the plays contained in the First Folio of 1623. This was the first collected edition of Shakespeare's plays and was gathered together by two of his fellow actors, John Hemmings and Henry Condell.

The Theatre in Shakespeare's Day

In 1989 an archaeological discovery was made on the south bank of the Thames that sent shivers of delight through the theatre world. A fragment of Shakespeare's own theatre, the Globe, where many of his plays were first performed, had been found.

This discovery has fuelled further interest in how Shakespeare himself conceived and staged his plays. We know a good deal already, and archaeology as well as documentary research will no doubt reveal more, but although we can only speculate on some of the details, we have a good idea of what the Elizabethan theatre-goer saw, heard and smelt when he went to see a play by William Shakespeare at the Globe.

It was an entirely different experience from anything we know today. Modern theatres have roofs to keep out the weather. If it rained on the Globe, forty per cent of the play-goers got wet. Audiences today sit on cushioned seats, and usually (especially if the play is by Shakespeare) watch and listen in respectful silence. In the Globe, the floor of the theatre was packed with a riotous crowd of garlic-reeking apprentices, house servants and artisans, who had each paid a penny to stand for the entire duration of the play, to buy nuts and apples from the food-sellers, to refresh themselves with bottled ale, relieve themselves, perhaps, into buckets by the back wall, to talk, cheer, catcall, clap and hiss if the play did not please them.

In the galleries that rose in curved tiers around the inside of the building sat those who could afford to pay two pennies for a seat, and the benefits of a roof over their heads. Here, the middle ranking citizens, the merchants, the sea captains, the clerks from the Inns of Court, would sit crammed into their small eighteen inch space and look down upon the 'groundlings' below. In the 'Lords' room', the rich and the great, noblemen and women, courtiers and foreign ambassadors had to pay sixpence each for the relative comfort and luxury of their exclusive position directly above the stage, where they smoked tobacco, and overlooked the rest.

We are used to a stage behind an arch, with wings on either side, from which the actors come on and into which they disappear. In the Globe, the stage was a platform thrusting out into the middle of the floor, and the audience, standing in the central yard, surrounded it on three sides. There were no wings. Three doors at the back of the stage were used for all exits and entrances. These were sometimes covered by a curtain, which could be used as a prop.

Today we sit in a darkened theatre or cinema, and look at a brilliantly lit stage or screen, or we sit at home in a small, private world of our own, watching a luminous television screen. The close-packed, rowdy crowd at the Globe, where the play started at two o'clock in the afternoon, had no artificial light to enhance their illusion. It was the words that moved them. They came to listen, rather than to see.

No dimming lights announced the start of the play. A blast from a trumpet and three sharp knocks warned the audience that the action was about to begin. In the broad daylight, the actor could see the audience as clearly as the audience could see him. He spoke directly to the crowd, and held them with his eyes, following their reactions. He could play up to the raucous laughter that greeted the comical, bawdy scenes, and gauge the emotional response to the higher flights of poetry. Sometimes he even improvised speeches of his own. He was surrounded by, enfolded by, his audience.

The stage itself would seem uncompromisingly bare to our eyes. There was no scenery. No painted backdrops suggested a forest, or a castle, or the sumptuous interior of a palace. Shakespeare painted the scenery with his words, and the imagination of the audience did the rest.

Props were brought onto the stage only when they were essential for the action. A bed would be carried on when a character needed to lie on it. A throne would be let down from above when a king needed to sit on it. Torches and lanterns would suggest that it was dark, but the main burden of persuading an audience, at three o'clock in the afternoon, that it was in fact the middle of the night, fell upon the language.

In our day, costume designers create a concept as part of the production of a play into which each costume fits. Shakespeare's actors were responsible for their own costumes. They would use what was to hand in the 'tiring house' (dressing room), or supplement it out of their own pockets. Classical, medieval and Tudor clothes could easily appear side by side in the same play.

441

No women actors appeared on a public stage until many years after Shakespeare's death, for at that time it would have been considered shameless. The parts of young girls were played by boys. The parts of older women were played by older men.

In 1613 the Globe theatre was set on fire by a spark from a cannon during a performance of Henry VIII, and it burnt to the ground. The actors, including Shakespeare himself, dug into their own pockets and paid for it to be rebuilt. The new theatre lasted until 1642, when it closed again. Now the Globe has risen again, after a committed band of actors, scholars and enthusiasts raised the money to rebuild Shakespeare's theatre in its original form a few yards from its previous site.

From the time when the first Globe theatre was built until today, Shakespeare's plays have been performed in a vast variety of languages, styles, costumes and techniques, on stage, on film, on television and in animated film. Shakespeare himself, working within the round wooden walls of his theatre, would have been astonished by it all.

PATRICK SPOTTISWOODE
Director, Globe Education,
Shakespeare's Globe